£3.40

FOR BOYS 1991

ALL THIS INSIDE —

ACE STORIES!

BRILL LAUGHS!

BRAINTEASERS!

PLUS LOTS MORE!

Printed and Published in Great Britain by
D.C. THOMSON & CO., LTD., 185 FLEET STREET,
LONDON EC4A 2HS.

ISBN 0-85116-477-3

THRILLS GALORE! MYSTERY! LAUGHS!
BLOOMIN' ADA, THEY'RE ALL HERE!
START NOW FOR A GREAT READ!
337
4
PUL SHUN
92

TOUGH
GOT TO HOLD OFF THE AUSSIE! CAN'T HAVE THE MILHAVEN TROPHY GOING DOWN-UNDER!
HE'S STICKING WITH ME! GOT TO SHAKE HIM OFF!

OF THE TRACK
Alf Tupper, the runner known as the Tough of the Track, was leading the field coming out of the last bend in the important Milhaven Mile. Hard on his heels was Joe Pale, an Australian star . . .
COME ON, ALF! RUN 'EM, LAD!
Suddenly a searing pain knifed from Alf's knee to thigh as an old injury re-asserted itself . . .
MY LEG! AAARGH!
ARE YOU OKAY, ALF?
FINE, MATE. I AIN'T MAKING EXCUSES. YOU RUN ME FAIR AND SQUARE.

WHO ARE YOU TRYING TO KID, ALF? THIS IS NOT THE FIRST TIME THAT LEG'S LET YOU DOWN, IS IT?
YOU'RE RIGHT, JOE. I FELL AWKWARDLY IN THE COLVERDALE MILE ABOUT EIGHTEEN MONTHS AGO. I THOUGHT I'D LICKED IT, BUT THIS LEFT THIGH'S BEEN GIVING ME TROUBLE LATELY.

I'VE HAD SEVERAL BLOKES LOOK AT IT, AND I'VE HAD A COURSE OF HEAT TREATMENT, BUT IT STILL HURTS.
WHAT YOU NEED IS KILL-OR-CURE KAPLAN TO SORT YOU OUT, ALF. CALLS HIMSELF A NATURE HEALER, BUT HE GETS RESULTS!

TELL ME MORE, JOE. WHERE DO I FIND THIS KAPLAN BLOKE?
HE HANGS OUT AT WONGA FLATS IN THE OUTBACK DOWN-UNDER. BUT I MUST WARN YOU, ALF — KAPLAN'S TREATMENT REALLY IS KILL OR CURE. HE'S COMPLETELY RUTHLESS. ONCE YOU'RE IN HIS HANDS THERE'LL BE NO ESCAPE UNTIL YOU'RE CURED — OR DEAD!

Alf wrote to Kaplan, who agreed to take him on. A few weeks later, Alf was working his passage to Australia on a cargo boat . . .
I JUST HOPE THIS KAPLAN BLOKE IS ALL JOE PALE CRACKS HIM UP TO BE.

From Sydney, Alf travelled north . . .
SURE I'VE HEARD OF KILL-OR-CURE KAPLAN, COBBER. A MATE OF MINE WENT TO HIM FOR TREATMENT A COUPLE OF YEARS BACK. HE HASN'T BEEN SEEN SINCE!
YOU'LL NOT SCARE ME OFF, MATE. I CAN TAKE ANY KIND OF TREATMENT IF IT'S GOING TO CURE MY GAMMY LEG.

IT DON'T LOOK LIKE KAPLAN'S SENT A RECEPTION COMMITTEE TO MEET YOU, COBBER.
WONGA FLATS 15 MILES
I AIN'T FUSSY, MATE. THANKS FOR THE LIFT.

Alf set off at a brisk walk, but the searing heat soon slowed him down . . .
BLOOMIN' ADA. YOU'D THINK THEY'D RUN A LOCAL BUS SERVICE IN THESE PARTS.

YOU ALF TUPPER — COME TO KAPLAN TRAINING CAMP?
THAT'S ME, MATE. AM I GLAD TO SEE YOU!
I SAM GANAGONG, KAPLAN'S CAMP MANAGER. I TAKE YOUR BAG. NOW YOU GIVE ME HANDS.
THANKS, SAM. I'M SURE READY FOR A RIDE.
I TAKE YOU TO KAPLAN'S CAMP.
HERE, WHAT THE HECK!
ARE YOU CRAZY? LET ME LOOSE!
KAPLAN LIKES PATIENTS TO KNOW WHAT THEY LET THEMSELVES IN FOR!
Alf ran till he almost dropped!
STOP, YOU CRAZY FOOL!
ALF TUPPER, KAPLAN!
GOOD ON YOU, SAM. WELCOME TO WONGA FLATS, ALF.
WHAT — WHAT'S WITH THE KNIFE?

CONTINUED ON PAGE 12

COLIN JACKSON

1. *Hurdler Colin Jackson is Scottish, English or Welsh?*
2. *Colin was World Junior 100 metres hurdles champion in 1984, 1985 or 1986?*
3. *Did he win a bronze, silver or gold medal in the Seoul Olympics?*
4. *In which event?*
5. *In February, 1989, Colin set the world indoor record for the 60 metres hurdles in a time of 6.84, 7.41 or 28.32 seconds?*

ANSWERS ON PAGE 63

CONTINUED FROM PAGE 10

Next day Alf was taken for a boat trip . . .
I'VE GOT TO HAND IT TO YOU, KAPLAN — MY LEG FEELS GREAT. I RECKON I'M CURED.
NOT YET, ALF. I SHALL TELL YOU WHEN YOU ARE CURED.

AREN'T YOU COMING ASHORE?
YOU ARE ONE NEEDING CURE, ALF. WE WATCH.

CAN'T SEE WHAT'S TO TEST MY REFLEXES HERE . . . BLOOMIN' ADA! CROCODILES!

YOU CRAZY FOOLS! GET ME OFF OF HERE BEFORE I'M EATEN ALIVE!

HOW'S THE LEG NOW, ALF? HOLDING UP, IS IT?

THAT DOES IT, KAPLAN! I'VE HAD ENOUGH OF YOUR CRAZY TREATMENT! I'M DISCHARGING MYSELF!

NOT TILL I SAY SO, ALF.

But Alf insisted he was fit, and to prove it he entered a 1500 metres race organised by the locals in Wonga Flats . . .

I'VE NEVER FELT BETTER IN MY LIFE. I'M NOT DANCING WITH ANY MORE CROCS — THAT'S FOR SURE!

Alf won in style . . .
YOU HAVE AWKWARD PATIENT HERE, KAPLAN.
I RUN 'EM!
SO IT SEEMS, SAM.
I SAY YOU ARE NOT YET FIT FOR COMPETITIVE RUNNING, ALF!
I SAY I AM! THE LOCALS TELL ME THERE IS A BIG ALL-COMERS' MILE RACE AT KAGOORY ON SATURDAY, AND I'M ENTERING FOR IT!
On Saturday at the Kagoory Stadium . . .
SAM! I DIDN'T KNOW YOU HAD ENTERED.
KAPLAN ASK ME TO KEEP AN EYE ON HIS PATIENT, ALF.
IT'S GOOD TO GET BACK ON A PROPER TRACK.
On the last lap, Alf broke from the pack . . .
HERE'S WHERE I SHOW KAPLAN HOW FIT I AM!
But under pressure from Sam, Alf felt twinges . . .
BLOOMIN' ADA! SAM MAKES IT LOOK AS IF I'M STANDING STILL!
CAN'T ACCELERATE! MY LEG'S NOT UP TO IT!

ALL RIGHT, KAPLAN. YOU WERE RIGHT AND I WAS WRONG. I'M STILL NOT FIT. WHAT NOW?
WE CONTINUE THE TREATMENT, COBBER!
So, thoughout the following week . . .
I'VE DONE EVERYTHING YOU'VE ASKED OF ME, KAPLAN, BUT THERE'S NO WAY YOU'RE GETTING ME BACK AMONGST THEM CROCS!
IT'S OKAY, ALF. TOMORROW IS KILL-OR-CURE DAY. YOU RACE SAM AGAIN — AND YOU RACE THE SUN.
Alf was wakened in the early hours and driven out into the desert with Sam . . .
YOU'RE THIRTY MILES FROM WONGA FLATS, ALF, AND IT'S ONE HOUR TO SUN-UP. YOU'VE NO WATER AND NO SHADE. IF YOU DON'T MAKE IT BEFORE THE SUN GETS HIGH . . .
. . . YOU'LL FRY, MAN — FRY!
NOW WAIT A BIT, KAPLAN! YOU COME BACK HERE!
SAVE YOUR BREATH, ALF. YOU'LL NEED IT!
THIRTY MILES AT THIS PACE?

Then sunrise . . .
IF HE CAN DO IT, SO CAN I!
. . . and the temperature rocketed!
THIS IS MAD — STARK, RAVING MAD!
Half blinded by sand and sweat, Alf battled on . . .
THERE'S WONGA FLATS! I CAN'T LET SAM BEAT ME AGAIN!
I'LL RUN HIM IF IT KILLS ME!
COME ON, ALF!
HE'S DONE IT!
WELL DONE, ALF. NOW YOU ARE FIT!
YOU COULD HAVE FOOLED ME, KAPLAN. I THOUGHT I WAS DEAD!
The End

MONSTER LAFFS

HA-HA-HEE-HEE!
CHUCKLE

You're sure of a good giggle after you've read the brill laffs below!

So get yourself comfortable and read on!

SHOES the CHEMIST
SUFFERING FROM A SORE THROAT? TRY "COUGHO DROPS"
WE'LL GUARANTEE YOU'LL NOT GET BETTER

What do vampires have every day at mid-morning?
A coffin break!!

Why did the monster visit the psychiatrist?
Because he thought everyone liked him!!

Teacher: Tommy, I asked you to write an essay on milk, and you've only written half a page when I expected much more. Why?
Tommy: *I wrote about condensed milk!!*

How does a monster count to 19?
On its fingers!!

How do monsters feel when they melt?
Abominable!!

What do you call a handsome, tidy, kind, considerate monster?
A failure!!

What goes out only at nights and can be heard saying, "Chomp, suck . . . ouch!"?
A vampire with a rotten fang!!

Did you hear what happened to the boy monster when he met the girl monster?
He fell in love at first fright!!

Diner: Waiter! Waiter! You've got your sleeve in my soup!
Waiter: *There's no arm in that, sir!!*

What do you do if you see six monsters running down the road towards you?
Hope they're late for a fancy dress party!!

OPEN SESAME!

OPEN SAYS A-WHO?!

DESERT PATROL

North Africa 1943, during the Second World War. German aircraft struck hard at a British Long Range Desert Group patrol . . .

Lieutenant Tom Slade was in command of one of the trucks . . .

STOP AND HELP THEM, PEARCE!

NO USE, SIR! THEY'VE HAD IT!

AAAH! WE'RE HIT!

ANOTHER MESSERSCHMITT! TAKE COVER IN THESE ROCKS!

The fiery Commanding Officer, Captain Mike Macey, appeared . . .
GET BACK TO YOUR TRUCK AND GET MOVING, LIEUTENANT SLADE!
Z

GETTING CLEAR OF THE TRUCKS IS THE USUAL DRILL FOR AIR ATTACKS.
NOT IN THE L.R.D.G.! WE KEEP MOVING AND WEAVING. WITHOUT TRANSPORT IN THE DESERT YOU'RE DEAD ANYWAY!

NOW MOVE OFF FAST!

NO STOPPING EVEN TO BURY OUR DEAD LADS, SIR?
THAT SEEMS TO BE CAPTAIN MACEY'S WAY. BESIDES, WE'RE BEING SHELLED NOW!

SCHNELL! FASTER! TRAP THE ENGLANDER DESERT RATS!

TEUFEL! THOSE RATS MOVE FAST!

The L.R.D.G. men made good their escape . . .
I THOUGHT YOU SAID THIS WAS A QUIET SECTOR, SIR!
IT USUALLY IS. SO WE NEED TO FIND OUT WHAT'S GOING ON HERE.

MARK FIVE PANZERS — OR EVEN TIGERS! HEAVY ARMOUR FOR THIS SECTOR. WE'LL TRAIL THEM.

It was Tom Slade's first mission with the L.R.D.G.
I DON'T RECKON CAPTAIN MACEY THINKS MUCH OF US FOUR, SIR.
PROBABLY NOT, CORPORAL! YOU A VOLUNTEER FROM THE SAPPERS, MYSELF AND THE OTHERS FROM THE ARTILLERY. HE PREFERS COMMANDO TYPES.

Suddenly . . .
A JERRY TANK HUNTER! IT'S GOT AN EIGHTY-EIGHT!
BEST GUN IN THIS WAR! PITY IT'S NOT ON OUR SIDE! SHOOT IT UP AS WE GO PAST!

TAKE THAT, FRITZ!

WE'VE AMMO TO SPARE FOR YOU, TOO!

BRITISHER SCHWEINHUNDS!

At dusk . . .
NOW WHAT DO YOU MAKE OF THAT, SERGEANT FRASER?
THAT OASIS SEEMS TO HAVE GROWN A BIT SINCE WE LAST SAW IT, SIR!

FAKE TREES AND CAMOUFLAGE! OLD AFRIKA KORPS TRICK.
TIGER TANKS MOVING IN, TOO!

THAT OASIS IS BEING BUILT UP AS AN ADVANCED PANZER CAMP LAAGER AND SUPPLY DUMP. EXPLAINS ALL THE NEW ENEMY ACTIVITY IN THIS SECTOR. IT'S UP TO US TO PUT A SPANNER IN THEIR WORKS!

WE NEED TO TAKE OUT THAT SENTRY — BUT QUIETLY.

URRGH!

SLADE, TAKE A FEW MEN TO PLANT OUR PLASTIC EXPLOSIVE CHARGES ON THE OIL AND PETROL STORES WHILE THE REST OF US CARRY OUT THE ASSAULT.
RIGHT, SIR.

ACHTUNG! BRITISHER RAIDERS!

Meanwhile Slade and his men were busy . . .
THIS IS MORE UP OUR STREET THAN KNIFING JERRY GUARDS, SIR!
Soon . . .
GET OUR TIGER PANZERS CLEAR!

THE TIGERS ARE MOVING OUT, CAPTAIN MACEY!
NOT MUCH WE CAN DO TO STOP THEM! BACK TO OUR TRUCKS!

Tom Slade also saw the Tigers rumbling forward . . .
THOSE TIGERS'LL BLOW OUR BLOKES' TRUCKS TO BLAZES!
BEST WAY TO HUNT TIGERS . . .

. . . IS WITH A TANK HUNTER! GUN CREW KILLED OR BOLTED. LET'S TAKE POST!

SO WE'RE BACK TO BEING GUNNERS!
FOR AS LONG AS JERRY LETS US!

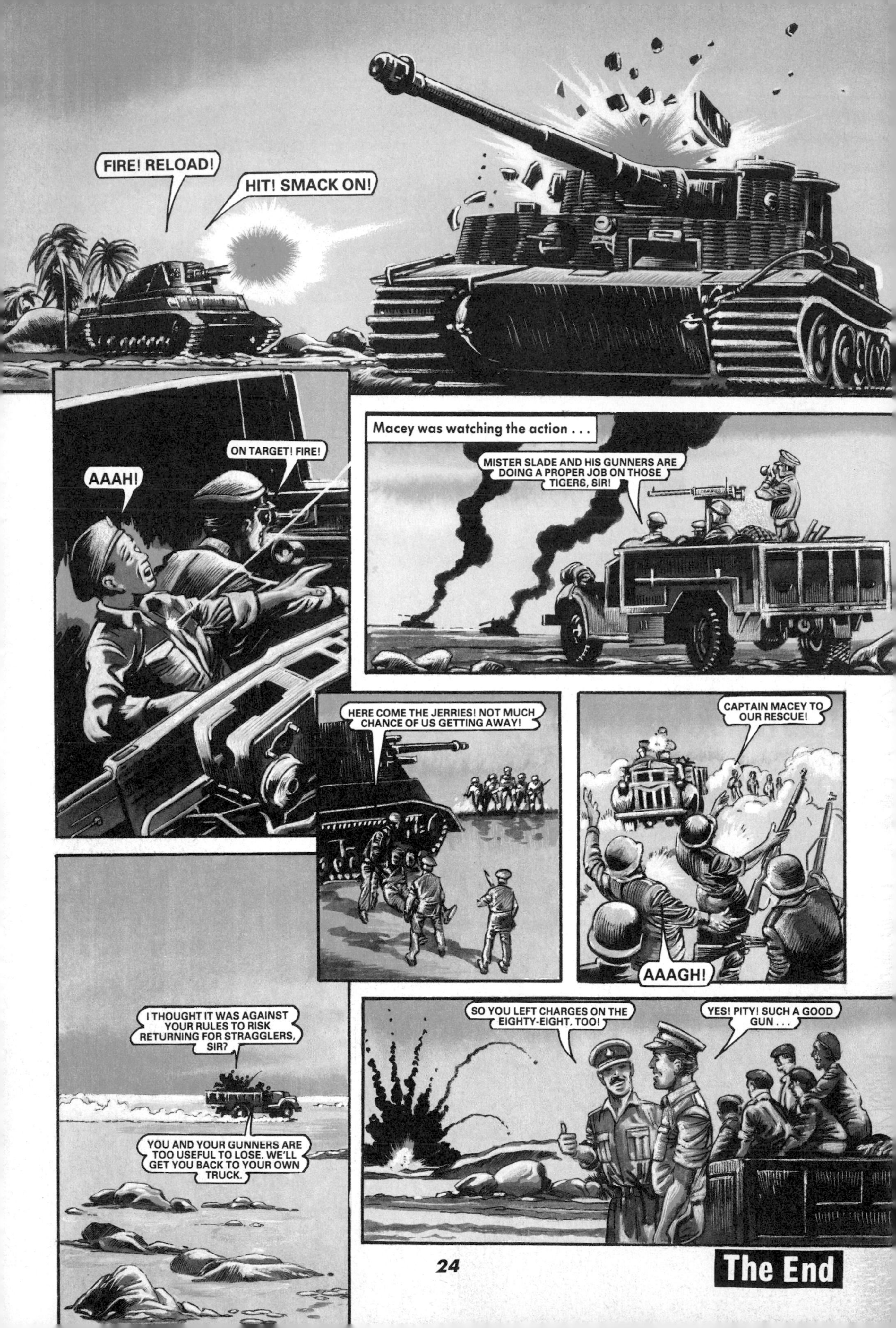

FIRE! RELOAD!
HIT! SMACK ON!

ON TARGET! FIRE!
AAAH!

Macey was watching the action . . .

MISTER SLADE AND HIS GUNNERS ARE DOING A PROPER JOB ON THOSE TIGERS, SIR!

HERE COME THE JERRIES! NOT MUCH CHANCE OF US GETTING AWAY!

CAPTAIN MACEY TO OUR RESCUE!
AAAGH!

I THOUGHT IT WAS AGAINST YOUR RULES TO RISK RETURNING FOR STRAGGLERS, SIR?
YOU AND YOUR GUNNERS ARE TOO USEFUL TO LOSE. WE'LL GET YOU BACK TO YOUR OWN TRUCK.

The End

BIKER

Gary Jones was the youngest rider in big-time motor-cycle racing. He rode for the small Sloan Sabre team, which was managed by his father. Now Gary found the going rough on a new track near Boulder City in Colorado, U.S.A. . . .

IT FEELS LIKE THEY LEFT SOME BOULDERS ON THE TRACK!

JONES AND HIS SABRE ARE STILL WAY OUT AHEAD!
HEY! WHAT'S THIS JOKER PLAYING AT?
HOLY CATS! HE'S GONNA BITE THE DUST RIGHT UNDER MY NOSE!
GOTTA GET HIM OFF THERE!
MUST GET CLEAR!
NEARLY MADE MANCINI CRASH!
GEE, I'M SORRY!

At the finish . . .
MANCINI WINS JUST AHEAD OF HEPPLER AND ROBSON! NO SIGN YET OF JONES AND THE BRITISH BIKE.
TEXAC
I HAD THAT RACE ALL SEWN UP, DAD, UNTIL THAT NUTTY KID CRASHED ME OUT OF IT!
SLOAN
SABRES
THAT LEAVES US JUST THE BIG INTERNATIONAL ON THE LAST DAY OF THESE TRACK-OPENING EVENTS.
I'M MATT NOLAN OF BLACKROCK RANCH. THAT WAS MY SON, RICK, WHO PULLED THAT FOOL STUNT ON HIS TRAIL BIKE. WE SURE OWE YOU AN APOLOGY . . . AND THANKS FOR SAVING HIS NECK.
SO HOW ABOUT STAYING AS GUESTS AT MY RANCH INSTEAD OF AT A MOTEL IN TOWN?
WE WON'T SAY 'NO' TO THAT!
So, later . . .
IS THIS WHAT'S CALLED A DUDE RANCH?
SURE! WE STILL RANCH SOME CATTLE BUT WE ALSO TAKE GUESTS FOR RIDING AND PLAYING COWBOYS.
Next day . . .
DAD WON'T LET ME RIDE THAT BIG BIKE YET.
CAN'T SAY I BLAME HIM, RICK!

WHY DID YOU PULL THAT NUTTY CAPER ON THE RACE TRACK, ANYWAY?
AW, SOME GUYS AT SCHOOL DARED ME TO TRY RACING YOU TOP RIDERS.
LOWER GEAR AND MORE RIGHT FIST, RICK!
SOME GUEST RIDERS FROM OUR RANCH OVER THERE.
I'LL GET SOME VIDEO FILM SHOTS OF ALL THIS WILD WEST SCENERY.
WHY ALL THE AGGRO WITH THOSE PONIES?
AW, HECK! THOSE SAND-BUGGY HOODLUMS AGAIN!
YAHOO! GIDDUP!
A BUNCH OF WILD GUYS HIRED BY FOLKS WHO AIM TO PUT OUR RANCH OUTA BUSINESS! THE LOCAL SHERIFF CAN'T DO MUCH ABOUT IT 'COS WE'VE GOT NO REAL EVIDENCE.
SO HOW ABOUT A VIDEO FILM TO PROVE IT?
THEY MUSTA SPOTTED YOU FILMING. BETTER SPLIT!

THEN IT'S ME THEY'LL CHASE! YOU GO THAT-A-WAY WHILE I GO THIS!
STOP OR WE'LL BLOW YOU AWAY!
THOSE JOKERS AREN'T FOOLING!
NASTY CRACKS IN THIS TRACK!
MISSED THE PUNK!
HE SURE CAN RIDE!
NOW THESE OTHER COMEDIANS ARE AIMING TO RAM ME!

SO SLAM ON THE ANCHORS, LAY THE BIKE DOWN AND LET 'EM WHIZZ PAST!
AAAH! GET ME OUTA HERE!
PRICKLY LANDING, PAL!
Soon, at the local sheriff's office . . .
THIS MAY PROVE THE AGGRO GOING ON AT THE NOLAN RANCH.
YOU SURE TOOK RISKS TANGLING WITH THAT WILD BUNCH, SON! MAYBE NOW I CAN MAKE SOME ARRESTS.
Next day . . .
BIKE'S IN GOOD NICK, GARY.
BETTER'N I FEEL! STRAINED MY LEFT LEG ON THOSE WILD WEST CAPERS YESTERDAY.
GOOD START FOR THE MAIN INTERNATIONAL PRIZE EVENT!
GOTTA SHUFFLE THROUGH THIS PACK.

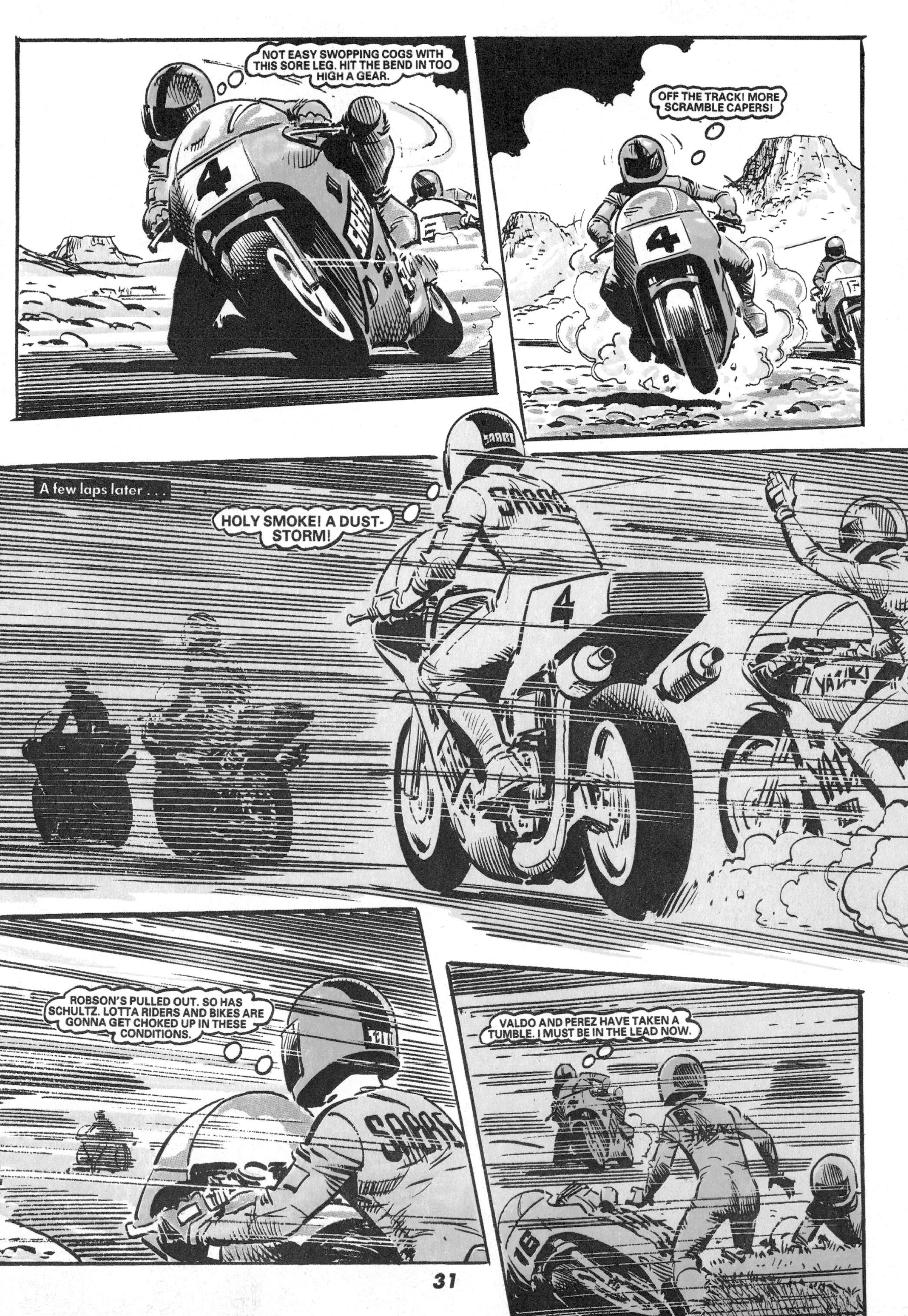
NOT EASY SWOPPING COGS WITH THIS SORE LEG. HIT THE BEND IN TOO HIGH A GEAR.
OFF THE TRACK! MORE SCRAMBLE CAPERS!
A few laps later . . .
HOLY SMOKE! A DUST-STORM!
ROBSON'S PULLED OUT. SO HAS SCHULTZ. LOTTA RIDERS AND BIKES ARE GONNA GET CHOKED UP IN THESE CONDITIONS.
VALDO AND PEREZ HAVE TAKEN A TUMBLE. I MUST BE IN THE LEAD NOW.

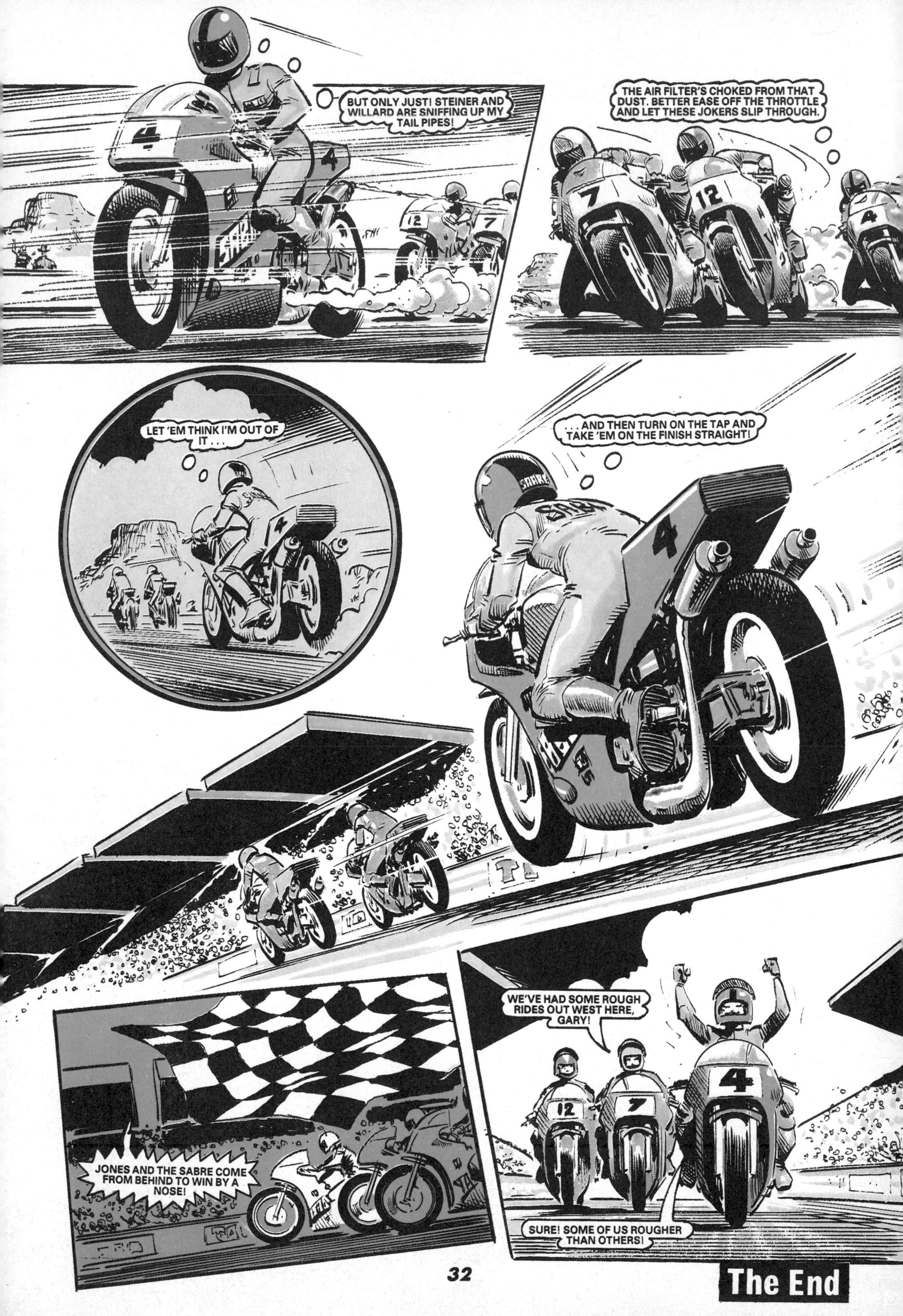
BUT ONLY JUST! STEINER AND WILLARD ARE SNIFFING UP MY TAIL PIPES!
THE AIR FILTER'S CHOKED FROM THAT DUST. BETTER EASE OFF THE THROTTLE AND LET THESE JOKERS SLIP THROUGH.
LET 'EM THINK I'M OUT OF IT . . .
. . . AND THEN TURN ON THE TAP AND TAKE 'EM ON THE FINISH STRAIGHT!
JONES AND THE SABRE COME FROM BEHIND TO WIN BY A NOSE!
WE'VE HAD SOME ROUGH RIDES OUT WEST HERE, GARY!
SURE! SOME OF US ROUGHER THAN OTHERS!
The End

VICTOR

QUICK QUIZ

NIGEL MANSELL

1. Racing driver Nigel Mansell won his first Grand Prix at Silverstone, Brands Hatch or San Marino?
2. The year was . . .?
3. Which racing team was Nigel driving for at that time?
4. He moved from that outfit to which other famous racing team?
5. Away from the racing track, is Nigel's favourite sport golf, hang-gliding or snooker?

ANSWERS ON PAGE 63

C

Tough conditions down a tin mine!

TOU OF THE TRACKS!

MOUNTAIN bikes have one big attraction — they'll take their riders practically anywhere they want to go.

A combination of low gearing and strong construction means that they can tackle the toughest slopes or roughest tracks with ease. As you can see from our picture, they've even been used to go cycling down a Cornish tin mine!

The mountain bike boom began over ten years ago in sunny California, where tough bikes with unusually wide tyres, lots of gears and super-strong frames were built to tackle the steep slopes and rocky tracks of the Sierra Nevada.

They were an instant hit, growing rapidly in popularity throughout America and, eventually, worldwide.

Now mountain biking has taken off in a big way in Britain. Cyclists just can't get enough of these distinctive machines, which are equally good for riding over pot-holed city roads or along the toughest tracks deep in the countryside.

What's more, mountain biking has developed into a fully-fledged sport, with national and world championships held annually and clubs opening up all over the country.

Above all, though, these bikes are for riders who are as tough as their machines!

Together, they've tackled some great adventures, like the team who cycled up a mountain Alf Tupper once conquered, Africa's Mount Kilimanjaro (although Alf did it on foot!). Or the bikers who made the punishing trip from London to Lagos!

And the toughest journey yet? Across one thousand miles of the Gobi desert! With a pedigree like that, these all-terrain bikes have proved they are real toughs of the tracks!

GHS

Action from the World Mountain Bike Championships.

Even top riders can bite the dust!

THE GOALS OF
The first match of England's South American tour and star striker Jimmy Grant was in the thick of the action against Verazala . . .
HIT THE BYE-LINE, PETER. THERE COULD BE AN OPENING HERE.
But . . .
ARE YOU THERE, JIMMY?

JIMMY GRANT

HIT THE BYE-LINE? I'LL BE LUCKY TO STAY ON MY FEET IN THESE CONDITIONS. THE WEATHER'S PROBABLY BETTER BACK IN ENGLAND!
He was!
IT'S THERE! JIMMY GRANT!
ONE-NIL TO ENGLAND!

YOU'LL NEVER GET BACK INTO ENGLAND, JIMMY. YOU DON'T LOOK A BIT LIKE YOUR PASSPORT PHOTO!
LEAVE IT OUT, PETER! IT'S WET, COLD AND MUDDY!
In the second half, Verazala put England under severe pressure . . .
COME ON, LADS! GIVE ME SOME COVER!
VERAZALA!
But two minutes later . . .
PERES SCORES! MAGNIFICO!
The move began with John Ball . . .
FIVE MINUTES TO GO. ONE LAST EFFORT! LET'S START THIS TOUR WITH A WIN!
GET AFTER THAT, THEN!
Jimmy collected . . .
IN THE MIDDLE, VINCE! QUICK!

YESSSSS! VINCE LAWLOR!
CAUGHT THEM NAPPING THERE!
Twenty minutes later . . .
STONE ME! LOOK AT THAT!
THE WHOLE TOWN'S FLOODED! THE RIVER'S BURST ITS BANKS! OUT THE FRONT WAY . . . THE COACH IS WAITING.
Two-one to England. After the match . . .
GET CLEANED UP AND CHANGED! WE'RE LEAVING IMMEDIATELY!
WHAT'S UP?
SOUNDS LIKE TROUBLE!
WHERE'RE WE GOING?
WE'RE FLYING OUT. OUR LUGGAGE HAS ALREADY GONE AHEAD.
HOPE IT'S A BIT DRIER IN URGALO!
WE WERE LUCKY TO START WITH A WIN TODAY! ON THAT PITCH, IT WAS ANYONE'S GAME!
San Jose City, Urgalo . . .
HOT IN HERE, ISN'T IT? HOW ABOUT NIPPING OUT FOR A WALK?
GOOD IDEA. LET'S GO!

But . . .
YOU NO LEAVE HOTEL, GENTLEMEN. ARMY EXERCISES. NOTHING TO WORRY ABOUT. TOMORROW YOU CAN GO OUT!
I DON'T BELIEVE IT!
AN ARMY DOESN'T HAVE EXERCISES IN THE MIDDLE OF A TOWN! WHAT'S GOING ON, BOSS?
DON'T ASK ME! THEY WON'T LET ME OUT, EITHER, NOT UNTIL WE GO TO SAN JOSE STADIUM TOMORROW.
Next day . . .
NOT MANY PEOPLE ABOUT! ONLY SOLDIERS!
MAYBE THEY'VE ALL GONE TO THE MATCH!
The stadium was half empty. The game was tough!
AAH!
FOUL, REF!
From the free kick . . .
SHOVE ON JIMMY GRANT!
THAT'S A PENALTY!
WHAT'S WRONG WITH THESE GUYS? THEY MUST KNOW THEY CAN'T GET AWAY WITH THIS STUFF!
THEY ALL SEEM VERY NERVOUS TO ME! STICK IT AWAY, JIMMY, AND LET'S GET ON WITH THE GAME.
YESSSSS! ONE UP TO ENGLAND!
THE CROWD . . . WHAT THERE IS OF THEM . . . SEEM TO BE ON OUR SIDE, ANYWAY!

The Urgalo team tried to hit back . . .

YES! OFF THE LINE!

SOUNDS LIKE THE CROWD DOESN'T WANT THE URGALO TEAM TO WIN!

Later . . .

OLE! OLE!

PETER'S GOING ALL THE WAY! NOBODY'LL GET A PASS FROM HIM WHILE HE'S ON A RUN LIKE THAT!

GOAL!

BEST BIT OF FOOTBALL THE CROWD HAS SEEN THIS AFTERNOON! THURSTON MAGIC!

A two-nil victory for England . . .

DON'T SAY WE'VE GOT TO GET OUT IN A HURRY AGAIN!

NOT ANOTHER FLOOD?

THIS TIME IT'S A REVOLUTION! REBELS ARE ATTACKING THE CITY!

THE ARMY WILL GET YOU SOUTH TO ARBRENTINA! WE GO BY ROAD! THE AIRPORT IS IN REBEL HANDS.

Trouble . . .
AN AMBUSH! IF WE STOP, EVERYONE WILL BE IMPRISONED!
GET YOUR HEADS DOWN IN THE BACK! AND HANG ON!

WE'RE THROUGH!
AAH!
THEY CAN SHOOT, BUT NOT AS WELL AS JIMMY GRANT! THAT LAD'S ALWAYS ON TARGET!
After a six hour journey . . .
ARBRENTINA! YOU WILL BE SAFE HERE!
NO TROUBLE!
NO SOLDIERS!
NO FLOODS!
Two days later, Arbrentina v England . . .
JULIO CAESAR SAVES EVERYTHING! HE MAGIC!
Jimmy had a chance, too!
JULIO CAESAR! YEAHHHH!
JULIO . . . HE MAGIC, ALL RIGHT!
In goal, Iron Barr had to do his stuff, too!
GREAT SAVE!
QUICK BALL!
GIMME TIME TO GET UP, THEN!

As full-time approached, England launched a last gasp attack . . .

ACROSS TO ME, PETER! QUICK!

LEAVE IT, VINCE! LET IT RUN!

IT'S THERE! ONE-NIL TO ENGLAND!

HARD LUCK, JULIO. YOU CAN'T STOP 'EM ALL!

A one-nil win for England . . .

NOT MANY GOALS. BUT A GOOD GAME!

I LIKE IT HERE! NICE PLACE!

WHAT'S UP? THE PLACE IS SHAKING!
OUT ON THE PITCH EVERYONE! IT'S AN EARTHQUAKE!

STONE THE CROWS! THE STAND'S COLLAPSING!
DON'T FANCY THIS!

Later . . .
BUILDINGS FALLING DOWN EVERYWHERE!
LET'S SEE IF WE CAN HELP!
After hours of frantic work . . .
OKAY, LADS, YOU'VE DONE YOUR BIT. THERE'S A RESCUE SQUAD ON THE WAY! WE'LL HEAD BACK TO OUR HOTEL. IT'S STILL STANDING.
Three day later, the England party arrived in Brazil . . .
THE PEOPLE OF ARBRENTINA CITY HAVE ASKED ME TO THANK YOU FOR YOUR HELP!
WE ARE NOT IN THE EARTHQUAKE ZONE HERE! YOU WILL BE SAFE IN RIO!
GLAD TO HEAR IT . . .
The last match of the tour . . .
BRAZIL! THE BIG ONE, LADS! AND A FULL HOUSE. LET'S SHOW THEM HOW ENGLAND CAN PLAY!
I'LL SETTLE FOR FINISHING THE MATCH WITHOUT AN EARTHQUAKE HITTING US!
YES, SOMEBODY MUST'VE WALKED UNDER A LADDER BEFORE WE CAME ON THIS TOUR!
The game was a classic . . .
ROZINO'S GOT IT! HE'S THROUGH!
THESE GUYS AREN'T JUST FAST — THEY'RE SUPER-SONIC!
YESSSS! ROZINO! MAGNIFICO!

Ten minutes later, Brazil scored again!
IRON BARR WON'T LIKE THAT MUCH!
GOOAAAALLL! RINOTO!
Just on half-time . . .
ROZINO! YEEESSSSSS!
THREE GOALS DOWN! THEY WERE ALL OVER US, BOSS!
THERE ISN'T A TEAM IN THE WORLD WHO COULD HAVE HELD THEM ON THAT DISPLAY! BUT THERE ARE TWO HALVES TO A FOOTBALL GAME!
Second half. An early stroke of luck for England . . .
THE KEEPER'S MISSED IT! WHERE'S JIMMY?
COME ON, ENGLAND!
GOT IT! THAT'S ONE BACK!
Five minutes later . . .
IT'S THERE! THREE-TWO NOW!

Brazil hit back!
ROZINO AGAIN! THAT'S HIS HAT-TRICK!
THAT WAS DOWN TO ME! I SHOULD HAVE CLEARED THE BALL EARLIER!
WE'RE ONLY TWO DOWN. WE CAN STILL DO IT!
Brazil thought they had the game won.
THAT'S GOING BEHIND!
IT'S NOT! HE'S STOPPED IT. GO TO HIM, PEDRO!
Too late!
IT'S THERE. JIMMY GRANT'S HEADER! FOUR-THREE!
WE'RE INTO INJURY TIME, JIMMY!
OKAY, THIS IS OUR LAST CHANCE! LET'S GO FOR IT!
Vince broke through . . .
WHAT A SAVE! MAGIC!

IT'S THERE NOW! JIMMY GRANT AGAIN! FOUR-FOUR!
FULL-TIME AND IT'S A DRAW!
TWO HAT-TRICKS IN ONE GAME. NOT BAD, EH?
NOT A BAD SCORE, EITHER, AMIGO!

In the dressing room . . .
ARRRRHHHH!
MAGNIFICENT DISPLAY, LADS. YOU WERE GREAT . . . HEY! WHAT'S THAT?
JIMMY! HE'S THE ONLY ONE IN THERE!

WHAT HAPPENED? HE'S OUT!
WASN'T AN EARTHQUAKE . . . OR FLOODING!
OR A REVOLUTION!

WHAT HAPPENED? I TROD ON THE SOAP! THAT'S WHAT!

WELL, IT'S BEEN AN EXCITING TOUR, JIMMY.
ENOUGH FOR A LIFE-TIME, BOSS!

The End

VICTOR QUICK QUIZ

PAUL McSTAY

(1) How tall is Paul McStay?
(2) He made his debut for Celtic in 1979, 1981 or 1982?
(3) He first played for Scotland in 1983, 1984 or 1986?
(4) Paul scored twice in the first World Cup match he ever played in. True or false?
(5) He was born in H---LT--. Can you name this town?

ANSWERS ON PAGE 63.

NIGHT STALKER
Four boys, Rob, Charlie, Hooky and Spots,were on a weekend walking tour. Suddenly . . .
ARHHHHHHH! I'VE SLIPPED!

SPOTS, STOP MESSING ABOUT AND GET OUT OF THERE.
HURRY UP, YOU FAT SLOB! WE'VE GOT MILES TO COVER.

Later, Spots took his turn at map reading and guided them past a deserted old mansion house.
SPOOKY, AIN'T IT? BRRR! THOSE WINDOWS ARE JUST LIKE EYES WATCHING US.
HERE — LET ME SEE THAT MAP. THERE WAS NO MANSION ON OUR ROUTE.

ROB, WE SHOULD HAVE TAKEN THAT PATH A COUPLE OF MILES BACK. I KNEW IT WAS A MISTAKE TRUSTING SPOTS WITH ANY MAP READING.

THE HARM'S DONE NOW AND WE AREN'T LIKELY TO REACH THAT HOSTEL TILL WELL INTO THE NIGHT. WE MAY AS WELL CAMP HERE.

NOT NEAR THAT OLD RUIN, ROB. THE LOOK OF THE DUMP GIVES ME THE CREEPS.

SUIT YOURSELF — SLEEP IN THE FOREST ON YOUR OWN TONIGHT.

ER . . . HOLD ON, LADS! I'M COMING!

THOSE WINDOWS DO LOOK LIKE WATCHING EYES.

LEAVE OFF, HOOKY. ONE SPOTS IS ENOUGH IN THIS BUNCH.

I DON'T FANCY THE ROOM SERVICE! WE'LL FIND A PLACE OUTSIDE.
THANK GOODNESS FOR THAT.
HEY, LOOK WHAT THIS SAYS. "HUWEL HOUSE, DESTROYED IN 1780 BY AN UPRISING OF LOCAL PEOPLE ENRAGED BY THE WICKEDNESS OF SIR RHYS HUWEL, KNOWN AS THE NIGHT STALKER, SUSPECTED OF MURDERING HIS NEPHEW TO STEAL HIS INHERITANCE AND WHOSE GHOST IS RUMOURED TO HAUNT THESE RUINS AT FULL MOON."
DIDN'T I SAY THIS DUMP WAS SPOOKY? ROB, LET'S FIND SOMEWHERE ELSE — PLEASE.
SPOTS, KINDLY SHUT UP AND MAKE YOURSELF USEFUL BY FINDING FIREWOOD.
The boys settled in as daylight faded.
FETCH WOOD, PEEL SPUDS — HOOKY, WHY IS IT ALWAYS ME DOING THE GRAFTING?
BECAUSE IT DOES YOU GOOD, YOU LAZY SLOB!
AARGH! WHAT'S THAT?
BATS, SPOTS — ONLY BATS. RELAX AND GET BUSY MAKING THE TEA.

Night fell.
LOOK! IT'S A FULL MOON!
THAT'S FINE, SPOTS. YOU WON'T NEED TO WASTE LAMP BATTERIES WHEN YOU DO THE WASHING UP!

In the night — an awakening.
I HEARD SOMETHING.
ME TOO.
AND ME.

A LIGHT — AND LISTEN!
MERCY, UNCLE! MERCY!

SOME BLOOMING JOKER HAVING FUN. WELL, I'M GOING TO FIND OUT WHO.
I'M WITH YOU, ROB.

HOW ABOUT WAKING SPOTS?
LET HIM SLEEP. IT'S ABOUT THE ONLY THING HE'S GOOD AT.

DARK AND QUIET, BUT THAT LIGHT AND THE VOICE CAME FROM IN HERE.
LET ME HAVE THE TORCH.

NOTHING HERE NOW.
LOOK OUT!

BLIMEY!

HERE COMES ANOTHER!

PHEW! THAT WAS CLOSE!

BLOKES, I DUNNO WHAT'S GOING ON, BUT MAYBE WE SHOULD PACK UP AND SCARPER!
I WON'T ARGUE WITH THAT.

WHERE'S SPOTS?
OUR PACKS ARE GONE TOO — AND ALL OUR GEAR.
HELP ME! HELP!
SPOTS' VOICE! COME ON.
IT'S COMING FROM DOWN THERE.
THE LIGHT'S GONE. CRIPES — WHAT'S THAT SPLASHING SOUND?
NO! NO! AHHHHHHH!
SPOTS' CAP!
THAT SPLASH MUST HAVE BEEN HIM GOING INTO THE WATER. THE FAT OINK CAN'T EVEN SWIM!
The boys stripped to the waist . . .
BRRR! IT'S COLD!

For five chilly minutes they splashed about.
NO SIGN OF HIM.
IN THE NAME OF . . .
URRRRH!
SPOTS!
IT'S ONLY FLOUR, MATES! HEE! HEE! I CERTAINLY HAD YOU GOING!
SPOTS — YOU'RE ALL RIGHT.
JUST MY LITTLE JOKES, MATE. I DIDN'T REALLY LOSE US. DAD AND MUM HAD A HOLIDAY CARAVAN NEAR HERE AND I PLAYED IN THIS OLD RUIN WHEN I WAS A KID. I RIGGED THE VOICE CASSETTES AND LIGHTS LAST WEEKEND AND ALL I HAD TO DO WAS SET THE TIMERS WHEN I WAS FINDING FIREWOOD.
THOUGHT I'D GET A BIT OF MY OWN BACK FOR YOU ALWAYS PICKING ON ME AND TREATING ME LIKE A DOGSBODY. JUST A JOKE. NO HARD FEELINGS, EH?
NO, SPOTS, WE CAN TAKE A JOKE . . .
GET HIM!
AARGH!

ONLY DROPPING THOSE ROCKS ON US WAS NO JOKE, SPOTS. WE COULD HAVE BEEN KILLED.
WHAT ROCKS ARE YOU TALKING ABOUT? I WOULDN'T DO ANYTHING LIKE THAT.

IF IT WASN'T YOU WHO DROPPED THOSE ROCKS, THEN WHO WAS IT?
HEY — LISTEN!

HAW! HAW! HAH! HAH! HAH!
LET'S GET OUT OF HERE!

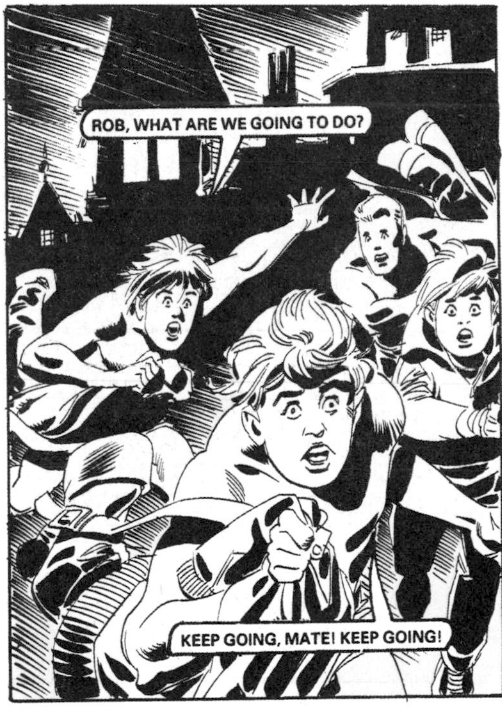
ROB, WHAT ARE WE GOING TO DO?
KEEP GOING, MATE! KEEP GOING!

Spots led them to where he had hidden their packs and soon . . .
WE COULD HAVE IMAGINED IT. PERHAPS IT WAS JUST NOISE MADE BY THE WIND OR THOSE BATS.
YOU THINK WHAT YOU LIKE, BUT I'M NOT STAYING TO FIND OUT!

HAH-HAH-HAH!
ROB, DO YOU HEAR SOMETHING?
NO, I DON'T! JUST KEEP GOING!
The End

CAN YOU SOLVE THIS CRIME BEFORE THE...
CRIMEBUSTER
TOP SPORTSMAN . . .
FAST MOVER . . .
AND MAN ABOUT TOWN . . .

Meet private detective Rick Chance, a modern day Sherlock Holmes. Case No.934 for the Chance Enquiry Agency gave him the chance to prove it!

It all began with the murder of businessman Roger Lee and the burning of his warehouse . . .
Months later, convicted killer Ben Nicklass burst into Rick's office . . .
MISTER CHANCE — ER — WE HAVE A PROBLEM.
A WELL-ARMED PROBLEM I SEE, WALTER.
GOT THIS OLD GUN IN A HOUSE I BROKE INTO, CHANCE. I'LL USE IT IF I HAVE TO.
I'M NOT LOOKING FOR HASSLE, FRIEND. TELL ME WHY YOU'RE HERE?
BLOKES IN PRISON SAID YOU'RE A TOP DETECTIVE. I'M BEN NICKLASS — YOU KNOW, THE LEE MURDER CASE. WELL, I DIDN'T DO IT AND YOU'RE GOING TO CLEAR ME . . .
I REMEMBER THE CASE, NICKLASS. IT STARTED WITH A TELEPHONE CALL TO A POLICE STATION . . .
YOU SAY YOU ARE MISTER LEE AND YOU SUSPECT A BREAK-IN AT YOUR WAREHOUSE ON KIRBY STREET.
HE'S INSIDE NOW. IT'S THAT MADMAN BEN NICKLASS — AND HE'S GOT A GUN!
DON'T, BEN — DON'T SHOOT! AAH!
BLIMEY!
"The police arrived on the scene in minutes, but the warehouse had gone up in smoke!"
WE'RE TOO LATE! NOBODY COULD SURVIVE IN THERE!
POLICE

TWO DAYS LATER THE EMBERS HAD COOLED ENOUGH TO BE SEARCHED, BUT NO BODY WAS FOUND. BY THIS TIME YOU WERE UNDER ARREST.
I DIDN'T KILL HIM. I FELT LIKE IT, BUT THAT'S NATURAL CONSIDERING HOW HE CHEATED ME OUT OF MY SHARE OF THE BUSINESS MY DAD AND HIS BUILT UP. IT WAS HIS IDEA I GO TO SEE HIM THAT SATURDAY AFTERNOON . . .

"I went ready for an argument, but Roger Lee surprised me . . ."
BEN, WE'VE HAD OUR DIFFERENCES, BUT THE FIRM'S EXPANDING AND I WANT YOU TO TAKE CHARGE OF A NEW WAREHOUSE I'M HAVING BUILT AT AN EAST COAST PORT.

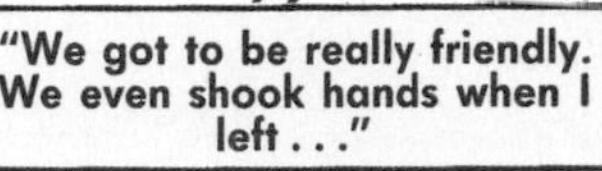
"We got to be really friendly. We even shook hands when I left . . ."
SO THAT'S IT ARRANGED, BEN — YOU'LL TAKE A QUICK LOOK AT THE SITE?
OKAY ROGER. I SHOULD BE ABLE TO GET THERE AND BACK BY TONIGHT.

"When I arrived home after looking over the site, I found the police waiting for me . . ."
DETECTIVE-INSPECTOR HAYMAN, SIR. I'D LIKE YOU TO ANSWER A FEW QUESTIONS ABOUT YOUR RECENT MOVEMENTS.
WHAT'S GOING ON?

"Then came a real shock . . ."
I FOUND THIS GUN IN THE BOOT, SIR — AND LOTS OF BLOOD!
I THINK YOU'D BETTER COME ALONG TO THE STATION WITH US, MR NICKLASS.

A GUN FOUND IN YOUR CAR BOOT, A MAN MISSING AFTER TELEPHONING YOU HAD COME TO SHOOT HIM! WHY NOT ADMIT IT? YOU SHOT ROGER LEE AND TOOK HIS BODY AWAY IN YOUR CAR TO BE DUMPED SOMEWHERE.
BUT IT'S NOT TRUE!

THEY NEVER DID FIND LEE'S BODY, BUT THERE WAS ENOUGH EVIDENCE TO ASSUME HIM DEAD ACCORDING TO THE JUDGE. SO I WAS JAILED FOR LIFE, ONLY I DIDN'T KILL HIM, I SWEAR.
INTERESTING. MISTER NICKLASS, I'LL TAKE ON YOUR CASE AND I'LL START MY ENQUIRIES RIGHT NOW.

JUST REMEMBER — NO POLICE OR I SHOOT. A GUY ALREADY DOING LIFE HAS NOTHING TO LOSE.
MISTER NICKLASS, I'LL DO MY BEST FOR YOU — BUT HARM THOSE TWO AND I'LL BE THE ONE FACING A MURDER CHARGE!
Rick looked up some court records . . .
HIGH COURT
ON THAT EVIDENCE, ANY JURY IN THE LAND WOULD'VE FOUND BEN NICKLASS GUILTY. NEXT STEP IS TO SEE ROGER LEE'S LAWYER . . .
T147B
ROGER LEE'S ESTATE PASSED TO A COUSIN LIVING IN THE MIDLANDS. THAT'S ALL I CAN TELL YOU.
THANKS FOR YOUR HELP.
Next came a chat with Detective Inspector Hayman . . .
DIDN'T YOU FIND IT STRANGE THAT THE MURDER WEAPON HAD BEEN KEPT, INSTEAD OF BEING LEFT WITH THE VANISHED BODY — ALSO THAT THE WAREHOUSE WAS SO WELL ABLAZE IN THE SHORT TIME IT TOOK THE POLICE TO ARRIVE?
THE SORT OF SILLY MISTAKES THAT MURDERERS ALWAYS MAKE, MISTER CHANCE.
Rick went back to his office . . .
I'VE KEPT MY WORD, MISTER NICKLASS — NO POLICE. I THINK I CAN HELP YOU, BUT ONLY IF YOU HAND OVER THAT GUN.
NO CHANCE.
OKAY, THEN I'LL DO IT THE HARD WAY.

NOW WE UNDERSTAND EACH OTHER, NICKLASS. LET'S GO FOR A DRIVE.

MISTER NICKLASS, YOUR PROBLEM WAS THAT YOU SEEMED SO OBVIOUSLY GUILTY, BUT IF YOU ARE INNOCENT WE'LL FIND OUT WHO THE REAL MURDERER IS VERY SOON.
T14

They stopped in a quiet village . . .
PIG AND WHIS
I'M LOOKING FOR A MAN CALLED HARRY TURNER. HE MOVED INTO THE VILLAGE THREE YEARS AGO.
HE'LL BE ON THE GREEN WITH THE BOWLS CLUB THIS TIME OF EVENING.

ANYBODY THERE YOU KNOW, MISTER NICKLASS?
NO— HEY! HOLD ON! THERE'S SOMETHING ABOUT THAT GUY WITH THE BALD HEAD . . .

GIVE HIM HAIR AND HE'S . . . NO, IT ISN'T POSSIBLE!
BUT IT IS, MISTER NICKLASS — AND HE SEEMS TO KNOW YOU.

HAVE YOU SOLVED THE MYSTERY? TURN TO PAGE 64 TO FIND OUT.

TOUGH

SOCCER QUIZ

Answer each of these soccer teasers in this crossword to reveal the name of an international football team in the dark grid.

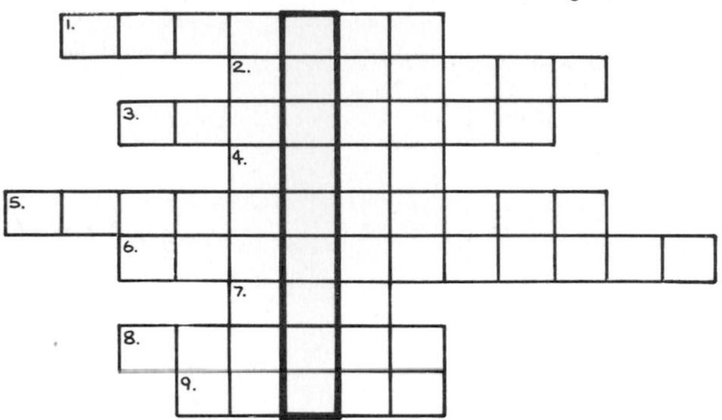

1. Ruud Gullit plays for what international team?
2. This country won the first World Cup back in 1930.
3. Brilliant Scottish internationalist who played for his country 102 times.
4. By what name was Edson Arantes do Nascimento better known?
5. This West German supremo captained the winning team in the '74 World Cup Finals. Who is he?
6. Which country hosted the 1988 European Championships?
7. England won the World Cup in 196-.
8. Michel Platini has played for and managed which country?
9. Where were the 14th World Cup Finals staged in 1990?

◀ *SEE QUESTION 5.*

BOBBY MOORE—CAPTAIN OF ENGLAND'S WORLD CUP WINNING SIDE. BUT IN WHAT YEAR? SEE QUESTION 7.

ROUND ONE

Answer each clue by starting with the first answer at 1. The last letter of each answer is the first letter of the next.

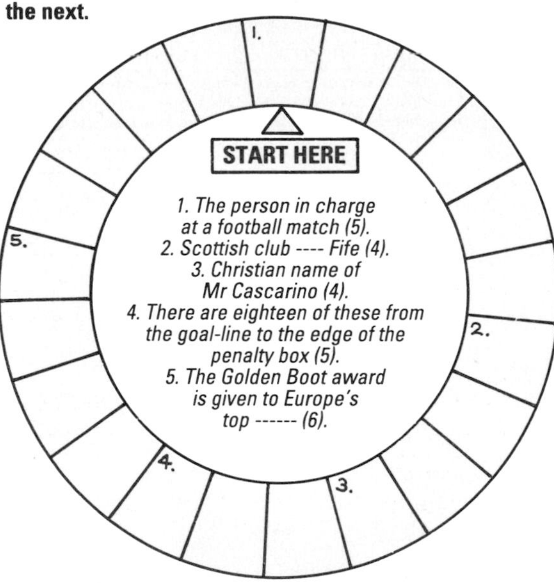

1. The person in charge at a football match (5).
2. Scottish club ---- Fife (4).
3. Christian name of Mr Cascarino (4).
4. There are eighteen of these from the goal-line to the edge of the penalty box (5).
5. The Golden Boot award is given to Europe's top ------ (6).

MAZE

Guide the cross country runner through the maze as quickly as possible to reach the finishing line in new world record time!

PICTURE PUZZLE

Decipher the clues below to reveal the name of a famous sportsperson.

TEASERS

SPOT THE DIFFERENCE

Study the two pictures and see if you can spot the six differences.

A

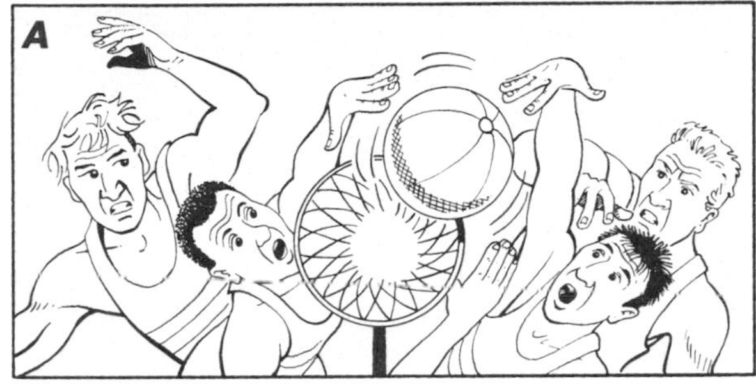

B

TRUE OR FALSE?

1. The first recorded Olympic Games took place in Greece in 776BC.
2. Glasgow Rangers are an older club than Glasgow Celtic.
3. Glen Hoddle and Chris Waddle once made a smash hit record together.
4. Severiano Ballesteros was once a trialist for Barcelona F.C.
5. Wales play their home international rugby matches at Cardiff Arms Park.
6. The America's Cup is a speedboat competition.
7. Starting blocks were illegal in the 1988 Seoul Olympic Games.
8. Boris Becker won the men's Wimbledon singles title in '85 and '86.

DELIBERATE MISTAKE

Study this scene showing an amateur boxing contest and try to figure out the deliberate mistake.

ANSWERS

QUICK QUIZ ANSWERS

COLIN JACKSON (PAGE 11)
1. — Welsh. 2. — 1986
3. — Silver. 4. — 110 metres hurdles. 5. — 7.41 seconds.

NIGEL MANSELL (PAGE 33)
1. — Brands Hatch.
2. — 1985. 3. — Williams.
4. — Ferrari. 5. — Golf. Nigel has even competed in the Australian Open.

PAUL McSTAY (PAGE 48)
1. — 5' 10". 2. — 1982.
3. — 1983. 4. — True.
5. — Hamilton.

MARK HUGHES (PAGE 119)
1. — Welsh. 2. — Attack.
3. — Barcelona.
4. — Sparky. 5. — 1985.

SOCCER QUIZ
1. Holland.
2. Uruguay.
3. Dalglish.
4. Pele.
5. Beckenbauer.
6. West Germany.
7. Six.
8. France.
9. Italy.

ARGENTINA.

ROUND ONE
1. Referee
2. East
3. Tony
4. Yards
5. Scorer

SPOT THE DIFFERENCE

PICTURE PUZZLE — Stephen Hendry.

TRUE OR FALSE
1. TRUE 2. TRUE 3. TRUE 4. FALSE 5. TRUE 6. FALSE 7. FALSE 8. TRUE

DELIBERATE MISTAKE
The boxers are not wearing vests — the difference between amateur and professional boxing.

CONTINUED FROM PAGE 61.

CADMAN
THE FRONT-LINE COWARD
VORWARTS! ATTACK!
GAD! THEY'RE ALL OVER US! GOT TO GET OUT OF HERE!
The Flanders battlefront during World War One. A daring German raid on the British trenches caught Captain Gerald Cadman V.C. badly by surprise . . .

E

Only Corporal Tom Smith knew Cadman for the cowardly rogue he really was.
NIP BACK BEHIND THAT TRAVERSE WALL, SIR.
AAH! NO!
SHOVE OFF, FRITZ!
GRENADES! GOT TO GET OUT TO THE REAR!
AAAGH!
HAVE YOUR OWN BACK, JERRIES!
STREWTH! MORE JERRIES AND THEY'VE CLOBBERED CAPTAIN CADMAN!
UURGH!
I'LL TAKE HIS PISTOL. IT'S HANDIER THAN A RIFLE IN THIS SORT OF LARK!

TOO MANY OF 'EM THOUGH!
GIVE UP, TOMMY!
AIN'T GOT MUCH CHOICE, FRITZ!
YOU AND YOUR OFFICER PUT UP A BRAVE FIGHT.
IF THIS JERRY OFFICER RECKONS OUR GALLANT CAPTAIN EVER FIRED THAT REVOLVER . . .
. . . THEN HE'S GOT IT ALL WRONG! NOT THAT IT MATTERS NOW.
BACK TO OUR LINES!
WHERE ARE WE? WHAT'S HAPPENING?
WE'RE OUT IN NO MAN'S LAND, SIR. JERRY'S BAGGED US.
Soon, at a German Command Post in a rear trench . . .
DO YOU KNOW WHY WE STAGED THAT RAID ON YOUR LINES, HERR CAPTAIN?
TO GET INFORMATION BY TAKING PRISONERS, HERR MAJOR? AND I CAN PROVIDE IT!

WE BELIEVE YOU PLAN A BIG OFFENSIVE ON THE DOULENS SECTOR IN A FEW DAYS TIME.
NO! IT WILL BE ON THIS ROUBAIX SECTOR, AT DAWN TOMORROW AFTER A SHORT BARRAGE.

DON'T TELL THEM THAT, YOU IDIOT!
HOW DARE YOU STRIKE YOUR OFFICER!

A CLEVER PRETENCE! BUT IT WILL NOT WORK! BRAVE SOLDIERS LIKE YOU DO NOT GIVE INFORMATION SO EASILY TO THE ENEMY!

BUT WHAT I TOLD YOU IS TRUE. IN RETURN FOR INFORMATION, I ASK FOR SPECIAL TREATMENT AS A VALUABLE PRISONER.
AFTER THE FIGHT HE PUT UP, COULD SUCH AN OFFICER BE A COWARDLY TRAITOR?

Later, in a German support trench . . .
THANK GOODNESS THOSE JERRY OFFICERS DIDN'T BELIEVE YOU!
I'LL CONVINCE THEM SOMEHOW, SMITH.

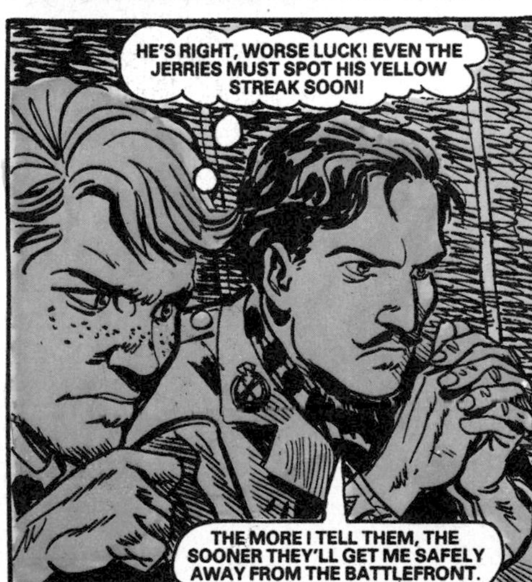
HE'S RIGHT, WORSE LUCK! EVEN THE JERRIES MUST SPOT HIS YELLOW STREAK SOON!
THE MORE I TELL THEM, THE SOONER THEY'LL GET ME SAFELY AWAY FROM THE BATTLEFRONT.

Suddenly . . .
ACHTUNG! BRITISH BARRAGE!
GET IN OUR DUG-OUT!

SORRY, FRITZ! I DON'T LIKE YOUR COCOA!
URRGH!
GAD! WHAT THE . . . ?
HIMMEL! I CAN'T SEE!
GET OUT OVER THE TOP, SIR, OR I'LL DO FOR YOU MYSELF!
KEEP GOING WHILE THAT SHELL-FIRE KEEPS THE JERRIES' HEADS DOWN!
YOU FOOL, SMITH! WE'RE NOT OUT IN NO MAN'S LAND HERE!
WE'RE BEHIND THE HUN FRONT LINES! HOW CAN WE POSSIBLY ESCAPE?
BLOWED IF I KNOW! BUT AT LEAST THE JERRIES'LL RECKON YOU MADE A BRAVE GO AT IT.
AND THAT'S WHAT THIS IS ALL ABOUT, SIR. MAKING SURE THE JERRIES DON'T BELIEVE THAT INFORMATION YOU BLABBED TO 'EM.
MACHINE-GUNS FIRING AT US NOW! WE'RE GOING TO DIE!
Then . . .
AIR ATTACK!
DON'T BE DAFT! IT'S MAKING A FORCED LANDING HERE. THAT'S WHY JERRY'S STOPPED FIRING.

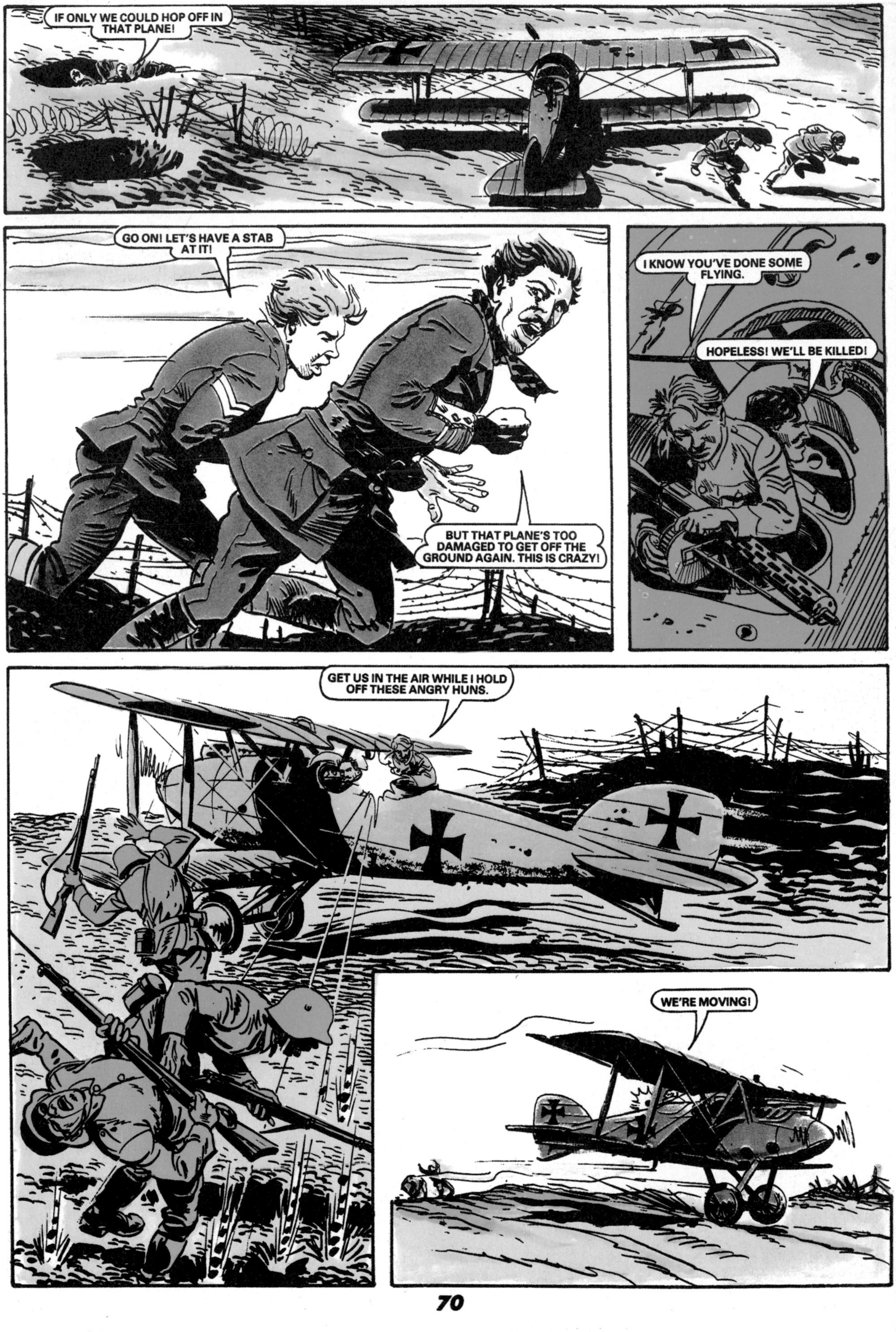

GET US IN THE AIR WHILE I HOLD OFF THESE ANGRY HUNS.

WE'RE MOVING!

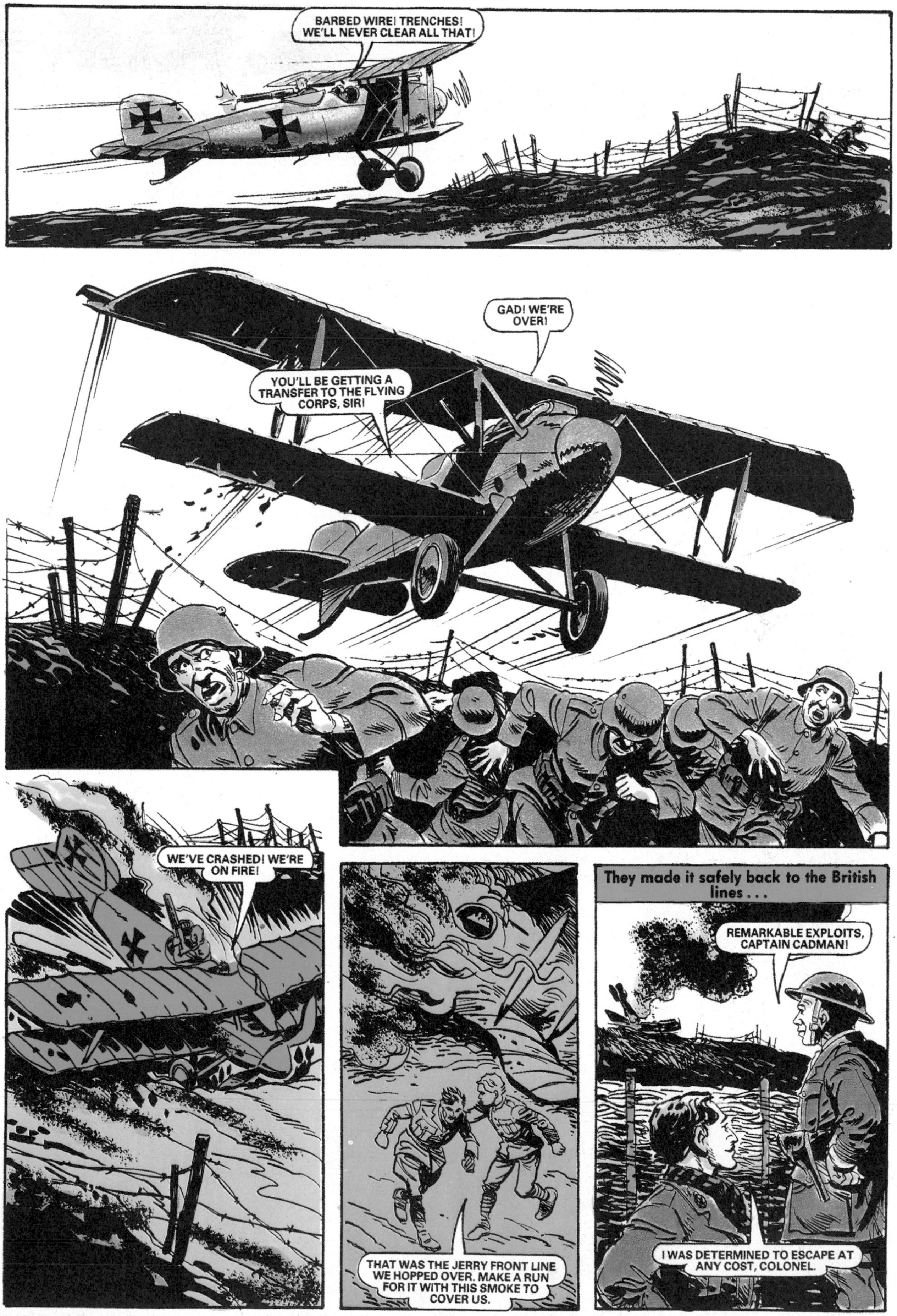

GAD! WE'RE OVER!

YOU'LL BE GETTING A TRANSFER TO THE FLYING CORPS, SIR!

The British offensive came next day at dawn . . .
WE'VE HAD IT IF JERRY GETS HIS MACHINE-GUNS ON PARADE AS USUAL!

IF JERRY'S EXPECTING US, IT'LL BE DUE TO THAT INFORMATION YOU BLABBED, SIR, AND I RECKON YOU'LL BE ONE OF OUR FIRST CASUALTIES.
BE QUIET, SMITH.

But soon . . .
KAMERAD! WE SURRENDER!
NO GUTS FOR A FIGHT, EH?

SEEMS THE JERRIES WERE EXPECTING US A FEW DAYS LATER. OUR SURPRISE ATTACK REALLY DID CATCH 'EM NAPPING THIS TIME.
AYE, BUT NO THANKS TO OUR GALLANT CAPTAIN.

WISH I HAD A CAMERA TO TAKE HIS PHOTO! MIGHT CHEER UP THE FOLKS BACK HOME TO SEE HOW OUR HERO IS WINNING THE WAR!

THE END

TERRY'S TORNADOES

Terry's Tornadoes, managed by thirteen-year-old Terry Miller, topped the Barnston Boys' League. With only three matches left to play, they could only be caught by their great rivals, Harold Mason's "Strollers". One day at practice . . .

NICE GOAL, BUNG!

YEAH! HOPE HE BUNGS 'EM IN LIKE THAT AGAINST HAGG STREET ON SATURDAY, TERRY!

THAT GEEZER'S BEEN WATCHING US FOR MOST OF THE TRAINING SESSION.

YEH, HE PROBABLY WISHES HE'D OUR SKILLS!

As they made their way home . . .
HE'S FOLLOWIN' US. ANOTHER KID'S JOINED HIM.

The youngsters caught up . . .
HEY, COULD MY BIG BROTHER GET A GAME WITH YOU LOT? HE'S A FANTASTIC PLAYER!
A GAME? LISTEN, KID, WE'RE THE TORNADOES . . . TOP OF THE LEAGUE! WE CAN'T JUST GIVE *ANYBODY* A GAME!

SHUT UP, GORDON. SORRY TO BOTHER YOU GUYS.
YEH, BUT WHO . . . I MEAN . . ?
On Saturday, against Hagg Street Panthers . . .
AARGH! BUNCHA BRUISERS!
FOUL, REF!
ONE NIL!
But the goal stood . . .
COME ON, GET STUCK INTO THEM!
THERE'S THAT GORDON KID.
NOTHING'S COMIN' OFF FOR US!
The Tornadoes again!
SHANE'S THROUGH!

PENALTY!
AARGH!
Only minutes remained . . .
GOT TO GET A DRAW AT LEAST. IF WE LOSE AND THE STROLLERS WIN THEIR GAME, WE'LL ONLY BE JOINT LEADERS!
OH, NO! I DON'T BELIEVE IT! I'VE MISSED!
Full-time, the score was one-nil and the Strollers had won on the other pitch.
MY BROTHER WOULDN'T HAVE MISSED THAT PENALTY!
OH YEAH — BLOOMIN' MARVEL HE IS! YOU OUGHT TO TELL THE ENGLAND MANAGER ABOUT HIM.
BUZZ OFF!
Shane's ankle was swollen badly . . .
IT WAS THAT TACKLE, TERRY . . . COR, IT'S MURDER!
GEE, SHANE, WE'D BETTER TAKE YOU TO HOSPITAL.

At Tornadoes' next practice . . .
I BROUGHT MY BOOTS ALONG. MY BROTHER SAID YOU NEEDED A STRIKER.
WELL, IF YOU'RE SURE IT AIN'T LIVERPOOL YOU REALLY WANT . . . LET'S SEE WHAT YOU CAN DO!
Garry Jones lived up to his brother's glowing opinion . . .
GEE, THE KID'S RIGHT — HE IS A *MARVEL!*
. . . he could head, dribble and shoot like a master!
And afterwards . . .
YOU'RE IN, MATE, NO QUESTION . . . SHANE WON'T BE FIT FOR OUR NEXT GAME OR THE LAST ONE AGAINST THE STROLLERS.
Garry played a stormer in their next game . . .
GOOD OLD GARRY!
YES! THREE NIL . . . GARRY'S HAT TRICK!
Three nil was the final score . . . and just as well — for the Strollers had won, too, keeping them on level points.

Next day . . .
WHAT'S YOUNG GORDON UP TO IN THERE?
Terry decided to investigate . . .
A RAT! THIS IS SOME DUMP!
GEE WHIZZ! LOOKS LIKE GARRY AND HIS BROTHER ARE STAYING HERE!
At training . . .
YOU'VE GOT SOME EXPLAINING TO DO, CHUM! WHY ARE YOU IN HIDING?
O . . . OKAY, YOU'D BETTER KNOW . . . WE'VE RUN AWAY FROM A CHILDREN'S HOME.
Gordon explained that he and Garry had been put in a home after their parents were killed in a car crash a few weeks earlier. There had been accommodation problems at the home and, fearing they'd be separated, they'd decided to run away.
WE'D SOME MONEY AND A FEW THINGS. I BROUGHT MY FOOTBALL BOOTS.
YOU WON'T SHOP US, WILL YOU?
COR, NO! WE NEED GARRY TO HELP US WIN THE LEAGUE!

The Tornadoes went out of their way to look after the runaways . . .
GEE, THIS IS A REAL FEAST YOU BROUGHT US, TERRY.
WE PUT OUR POCKET MONEY TOGETHER.
THANKS, OUR FAVE UNCLE'LL BE HOME FROM THE NAVY SOON, FOR GOOD. IF WE CAN JUST LAST OUT TILL THEN, HE'LL TAKE US TO LIVE WITH HIM.
In their final game, the Tornadoes were away to their old rivals the Strollers, captained by Harold Mason —
YOU'LL HAVE TO BEAT US, MILLER! WE'RE AHEAD ON GOAL DIFFERENCE. A DRAW'S NO USE TO YOU!
WE'LL WHITEWASH YOU, MASON.
Garry struck form right away . . .
HEY, HAVEN'T I SEEN HIS FACE SOMEWHERE BEFORE?
COULD BE, MATE. HE GOES TO THE SCHOOL NEXT TO US. PASSES THE GATES EVERY MORNING.
No score after twenty minutes, then . . .
AW, NO! A DEFLECTION! GINGER HAD NO CHANCE!
Into the second half — a snap shot from Garry . . .
YE . . . ES, GREAT GOAL, GARRY! ME BROTHER'S FANTASTIC!
GARRY . . . GARRY? THAT KID'S FAMILIAR, TOO, SOMEHOW . . .

THEY'RE RUNAWAYS! I SAW THEIR FACES ON A "MISSING" POSTER! I MUST TELL THAT POLICEMAN BEFORE HE MOVES OFF.

OH, NO YOU DON'T!

AARGH!

I THINK HE'S HURT HIS ANKLE, REF! BEST GET THEIR TRAINER!

SORRY!

I HAVEN'T! LET ME *UP*!

POLICE! I WANT THE POLICE!
NOW, NOW, SON. NO NEED TO BE LIKE THAT. IT WAS JUST A FOUL! HANG ON TILL SOMEBODY LOOKS AT YOUR ANKLE.
YOU IDIOT! THE POLICEMAN'S DISAPPEARED!
GET ON WITH THE GAME!
YES, COME ON, HAROLD! WE'VE NO TIME TO SPARE!

I'LL SHOP THAT GARRY FIRST CHANCE I GET. BUT WE'RE UNDER TOO MUCH PRESSURE RIGHT NOW!
HE'S A RUNAWAY, CONSTABLE!
I CAN SEE THAT, SON. YOU'D BETTER STOP HIM! HA-HA!
A neat pass to Terry and . . .
TWO ONE!
YOU SHOULD HAVE TACKLED, HAROLD, INSTEAD OF SHOUTING AT THAT POLICEMAN!
By the time Harold told the policeman . . .
THREE ONE! ALMOST ON FULL-TIME! WE'VE WON THE LEAGUE!
Afterwards the policeman radioed in to tell the lads that their uncle had already flown home and was on his way to collect them.
ISN'T IT GREAT? LEAGUE WINNERS' MEDALS AND NOW OUR UNCLE'S ON HIS WAY TO SET UP A HOME FOR US!
YOU'RE A GOOD PLAYER, TOO, TERRY.
THANKS, GORDON. WE SURE WOULDN'T HAVE WON WITHOUT GARRY. MAYBE HE WILL PLAY FOR ENGLAND ONE DAY . . .
THE END

IT'S GOALIES THAT COUNT!

The great entertainer — Liverpool's Bruce Grobbelaar.

They play under tremendous pressure. They are constantly criticised for every mistake they make. But top strikers like Jimmy Grant and Bung know just what a vital role keepers play in any successful team.

When the chips are down, it's goalies that count!

Hands like glue! Norwich goalie Bryan Gunn is a top class performer.

The keeper many players rate as the best in Britain — Welsh international Neville Southall.

"This one's mine!" says Rangers keeper Chris Woods.

THEY CAN'T
During a brief lull in the fighting, Cook Darren Philips was relieved from his action station on the bridge phones to perform another task . . .
"WHAT DID YOU DO IN THE WAR, DADDY, WHEN THE GUNS WERE BLAZING AND THE BOMBS WERE DROPPING?" "ME, SON? I MADE THE TEA!"
STOP YOUR BELLY-ACHING, DARREN. WHEN THIS WAR'S OVER SOMEBODY WILL ASK WHAT WON THE WAR FOR US AND THE ANSWER WILL BE THE GOOD OLD BRITISH CUPPA!

KILL SANTA!
On December 24th, 1941, the British Naval Base at Hong Kong was besieged by Japanese forces. The evacuation of wives and children of shore-based personnel was almost complete. The frigate H.M.S. Runcorn was standing by to take off those who remained . . .
LET'S HOPE WE CAN GET AWAY BEFORE DARK, NUMBER ONE. IT'S GOING TO BE ONE HECK OF A JOB PICKING OUR WAY ROUND THOSE WRECKS.
COMMANDER HICKS ESTIMATES ABOUT TWO MORE HOURS, SIR.
TEA, SIR.

AH, PHILIPS — JUST THE MAN. I'VE GOT A SPECIAL MISSION FOR YOU. REPORT TO THE GUNNERY OFFICER.
ME, SIR? AYE, AYE, SIR!

Darren was excited. He was keen to get a real, fighting job. Perhaps there had been a casualty on the for'ard Oerlikon, or the multiple pom-pom . . .
COOK PHILIPS REPORTING FOR DUTY, SIR!
GOOD, YOU'RE ABOUT MY SIZE. COME IN, LAD.

I WANT YOU TO TAKE OVER MY JOB, LAD. HERE, PUT THIS ON.
BUT — BUT IT'S A SANTA CLAUS OUTFIT, SIR!

IN CASE YOU'D FORGOTTEN, PHILIPS, IT'S CHRISTMAS EVE. WE PLANNED A PARTY FOR THE KIDS AT BASE H.Q. MONTHS AGO. I WAS GOING TO BE SANTA CLAUS AND DISH OUT THE GIFTS.
BUT, SIR, THINGS HAVE CHANGED! THERE'S A WAR ON!

SOME OF THE KIDS ARE SHELTERING IN THE CELLARS AT THE HOON SIGH BUILDING UNTIL WE CAN TAKE THEM OUT. THEY ARE SCARED STIFF. THE ARRIVAL OF SANTA WITH THEIR PRESENTS COULD TAKE THEIR MINDS OFF THE BOMBING. NOW GET GOING!
AYE, AYE, SIR.
WHO SAYS THERE AIN'T NO SANTA CLAUS! WHERE'S YOUR REINDEER, DARREN? HA! HA! HA!

At the Hoon Sigh building . . .
WHERE ARE THESE KIDS, MATE?
IN THE CELLAR. FIRST DOOR ON YOUR RIGHT AND DOWN THE STEPS.
AW, COME ON, SANTA. SHOULDN'T YOU BE GOING DOWN THE CHIMNEY?

THERE'S BEEN A CHANGE OF PLAN THIS YEAR, MATE!
LOOK OUT! A JAP PLANE!

BLIMEY — THAT WAS CLOSE!

HO! HO! HO! HAPPY CHRISTMAS EVERYONE!
LOOK WHO'S HERE, CHILDREN! DIDN'T I TELL YOU HE WOULDN'T FORGET YOU?

YOU DON'T WANT TO WORRY ABOUT THOSE AEROPLANES OUT THERE, KIDS. THEY DIDN'T STOP ME GETTING HERE ALL THE WAY FROM GREENLAND, NOW DID THEY?

I'M SO GLAD YOU CAME. YOU DON'T KNOW WHAT THIS MEANS TO US. DO YOU KNOW WHEN WE ARE TO BE TAKEN OUT?
SHOULDN'T BE LONG NOW, MA'AM. A COUPLE MORE HOURS, I HEARD.
Meanwhile the raiders had returned . . .
GOT YOU, YOU PERISHER!
The stricken plane crashed into the Hoon Sigh building!
In the cellar . . .
COME ON, EVERYBODY — WE'VE GOT TO GET OUT OF HERE!

Darren removed his whiskers . . .
STAY CLOSE TOGETHER AND FOLLOW ME!
Aboard the Runcorn . . .
MESSAGE FROM BASE H.Q, SIR — SAIL IMMEDIATELY!
VERY WELL, NUMBER ONE. PREPARE TO CAST OFF! PITY, I'D HOPED TO WAIT FOR THESE KIDS, BUT I'D BE HAZARDING THE SHIP IF I DID.
The women and children were bundled below . . .
WAIT, DARN YOU! WAIT!
WE'RE IN LUCK! THERE'S A DINGHY UNDAMAGED!
COME ON, KIDS! PILE IN! HURRY!
THIS WAY, CHILDREN! DON'T BE AFRAID!

SHE'S WAITING FOR US! THEY'RE PUTTING OUT SCRAMBLE NETTING.
AAGH!
HOW BAD IS IT, PHILIPS?
I RECKON I'LL LIVE, SIR.
GET THEM ABOARD, QUICKLY!
PHILIPS HAS BEEN HIT, SIR!
THEM NIPS CAN DO THEIR WORST — BUT THEY CAN'T KILL SANTA!
The End

ACTION STATIONS

A TRUE WAR STORY

Towards the end of 1941, during the Second World War, Lieutenant David Stirling was given permission to form a special unit of his own. This was the start of the Special Air Service and it was to become a unit more feared by the Germans and Italians in the Western Desert than any other. In their heavily armed jeeps the S.A.S. ranged far behind the enemy lines, shooting up airfields and convoys and generally disrupting the enemy's lines of communications.

One of their most daring raids was the attack on Sidi Haneish, one moon-lit night in August 1942. Sidi Haneish was one of the Germans' main staging aerodromes in the Western Desert and was far behind the front line. After the German garrison had settled down for the night, eighteen jeeps raced on to the aerodrome and, making a sweep right round the perimeter, shot up every plane in sight.

Leaving the blazing airfield they raced back into the desert, leaving a completely demoralised enemy behind them. For the loss of two jeeps they had destroyed between forty and fifty German aircraft.

DAVID STIRLING

The Willys jeep as used by the S.A.S., equipped with two Vickers K machine-guns and a Browning machine-gun.

TORO
SPACE SAMURAI

It is the future. The ship of space-age Samurai Toro Tanaka and his crewman Rat was shifting from hyperflight into sublight drive when another vessel was detected by her instruments . . .

HEY, RAT, SHIPLOG HAS PICKED UP A SHIP MOVING INTO THE VORTEX OF THAT BLACK HOLE!

I SEE HER, BOSS! THERE SHE GOES!

SHIPLOG TO PERSONNEL. I DETECT PARTICLE DRIVE POWERED BY CRUDE FORM OF HYDROGEN FUSION. DATABASE HOLDS NO RECORD OF ANY SUCH CLASS OF VEHICLE.
WE'LL GO IN FOR A CLOSER LOOK, RAT.

Approaching the black hole — the spectacular collapse of a star — was a deadly business!
THE SHIP'S SO BIG, CHIEF — AND SO OLD. THAT TYPE OF DRIVE HASN'T BEEN USED FOR OVER A THOUSAND YEARS.
COULD BE A DERELICT, RAT — BUT IF IT HAS BEEN ABANDONED, WHY HASN'T THE POWER PILE BEEN DAMPENED?
WARNING TO CREW! OTHER VEHICLE WILL REACH POINT OF NO RETURN IN THIRTY-FIVE STANDARD MINUTES.
SHIPLOG REPORT. SCAN DETECTS EVIDENCE OF BIOLOGICAL LIFE ABOARD.
LIVING ORGANISMS! RAT, I'M GOING ABOARD.
IT'S NOT OFTEN YOU VOLUNTEER FOR A SPACE-TREK, RAT.
I WON'T MAKE A HABIT OF IT, BUT YOU MIGHT NEED AN ENGINEER OVER THERE.
SHIPLOG TO PERSONNEL! REM COUNT INDICATES VEHICLE HAS MADE PASSAGE THROUGH HEAVY RADIATION. THE SAFETY TOLERANCE OF YOUR ARMOUR IS ONE STANDARD HOUR.

Toro and Rat boarded the mystery ship.
OUTER HATCH SEALED, TORO.
I'M CRACKING THE INNER HATCH NOW.
AIR CAPABLE OF HUMAN LIFE-SUPPORT, BUT THE GEIGER COUNTER'S GOING CRAZY. WE'LL STICK TO OUR PERSONAL BREATHING SUPPLY.
SHIPLOG TO PERSONNEL! YOUR BEACONS LOCATE YOU ABOARD MIDSHIPS AREA. BIOLOGICAL LIFE IN YOUR VICINITY, BUT MOVING AND EVASIVE.
EVASIVE IS RIGHT, BOSS. NO SIGN OF ANY MOVEMENT, BUT MY EARPHONES ARE PICKING UP NOISES — RUSTLINGS AND SQUEAKING.
WHOEVER IT IS HAD BETTER STOP BEING SHY IF WE'RE TO HELP THEM.
A HUMAN SKULL!
CRUMBLING WITH AGE. MUST HAVE TAKEN A COUPLE OF HUNDRED YEARS TO GET LIKE THAT IN MICROBE-FREE CONDITIONS.
I GET IT NOW. THIS IS A COLONY SHIP FROM WHEN OLD EARTH WAS GETTING POLLUTED — ONE OF THE TRANSPORTS PACKED WITH FOLK IN DEEP FREEZE WHICH WENT CHUGGING OUT IN HOPE OF FINDING PLANETS TO SETTLE.
THIS ONE MUST HAVE ESCAPED THE ROUND-UP WHEN HYPERFLIGHT WAS DISCOVERED AND WE COULD SKIP ABOUT THE GALAXY.

SO THIS SHIP JUST PLODDED ON WITH A FROZEN CARGO — AND NOW WE COME ON IT AND THE FREEZER CABINETS ARE BROKEN OPEN AND EMPTY.
SOMETHING HAS SURVIVED. THERE IS SOMETHING LIVING ON THIS TUB.
Suddenly, there was sound and movement!
TROUBLE!
WHAT KIND OF COLONISTS ARE THESE?
TORO! HELP ME!
I'M COMING, RAT.

But when the shaggy swarm vanished, Toro was alone!
I'LL FIND YOU, RAT.
HURRY, CHIEF! HURRY!
WHATEVER THEY ARE, THEY'RE NOT HUMAN, SHIPLOG — SO WHAT ARE THEY?
DATABASE COMMENCING RESEARCH.
LIFEFORM A MUTATED FORM OF TELURIANRODENT, TERMED RATTUS-RATTUS OR RAT, THE EVOLUTIONARY CHANGE DUE TO EXPOSURE TO RADIATION.
YOU MEAN OUR RAT HAS BEEN TAKEN BY A PACK OF TWO-LEGGED RATS!
THAT IS A LOGICAL DEDUCTION.
YOU ARE PROCEEDING IN CORRECT DIRECTION, BUT RAT'S BEACON IS LOCATED AT HIGHER LEVEL.
I'VE COME ON A GANGWAY TO THE DECK ABOVE.
YOU ARE VERY CLOSE.
TROUBLE IS THERE'S A BULKHEAD IN THE WAY.
RAT! DO YOU HEAR ME?
I HEAR YOU, CHIEF. BUT HURRY! THERE'S A WHOLE PACK OF THEM ROUND ME AND I'VE GOT A FEELING THEY'RE NONE TOO FRIENDLY.
SHIPLOG TO PERSONNEL. YOU HAVE FIVE STANDARD MINUTES BEFORE BOTH VEHICLES REACH POINT OF NO RETURN IN JOURNEY TO CENTRE OF BLACK HOLE.
THEN WE'VE GOT TO WORK FAST. DRAW THE CHARGE FROM THE HEAD OF ONE OF THOSE CHEMICAL MISSILES AND AIM FOR A NEAR MISS ON RAT'S BEACON.

Within seconds . . .
MISSILE DISCHARGED.
RAT, HOLD ON TO SOMETHING. BRACE FOR DECOMPRESSION.
The missile tore through the stern of the old transport ship.
I AIN'T ENJOYING THIS, BUT THE RAT CREATURES ARE ENJOYING IT EVEN LESS!
RAT, I'M COMING THROUGH. ARE YOU ALL RIGHT? ANSWER ME!
I'M ALL RIGHT, CHIEF.
THEN LET'S GET OUT OF THIS HULK. RIGHT NOW!
SO THAT'S WHAT SUPER RATS ARE LIKE! FROM NOW ON, BOSS, I'D RATHER BE CALLED BY MY FULL NAME OF RATTIGAN!
The patroller tore free of the grip of the black hole's vortex!
THERE IS AN OLD EARTH LEGEND ABOUT RATS BEING FIRST TO LEAVE A SINKING SHIP. THAT PACK APPEARS TO HAVE DELAYED DEPARTURE TOO LONG.
The End

MORGYN the MIGHTY
Morgyn the Mighty, the strongest man in the world, never looked for trouble, but at times he was forced to defend himself — as when he was unexpectedly attacked by one of the giant monitor lizards of the Pacific island of Komodo . . .
KEEP YOUR DISTANCE, FRIEND!

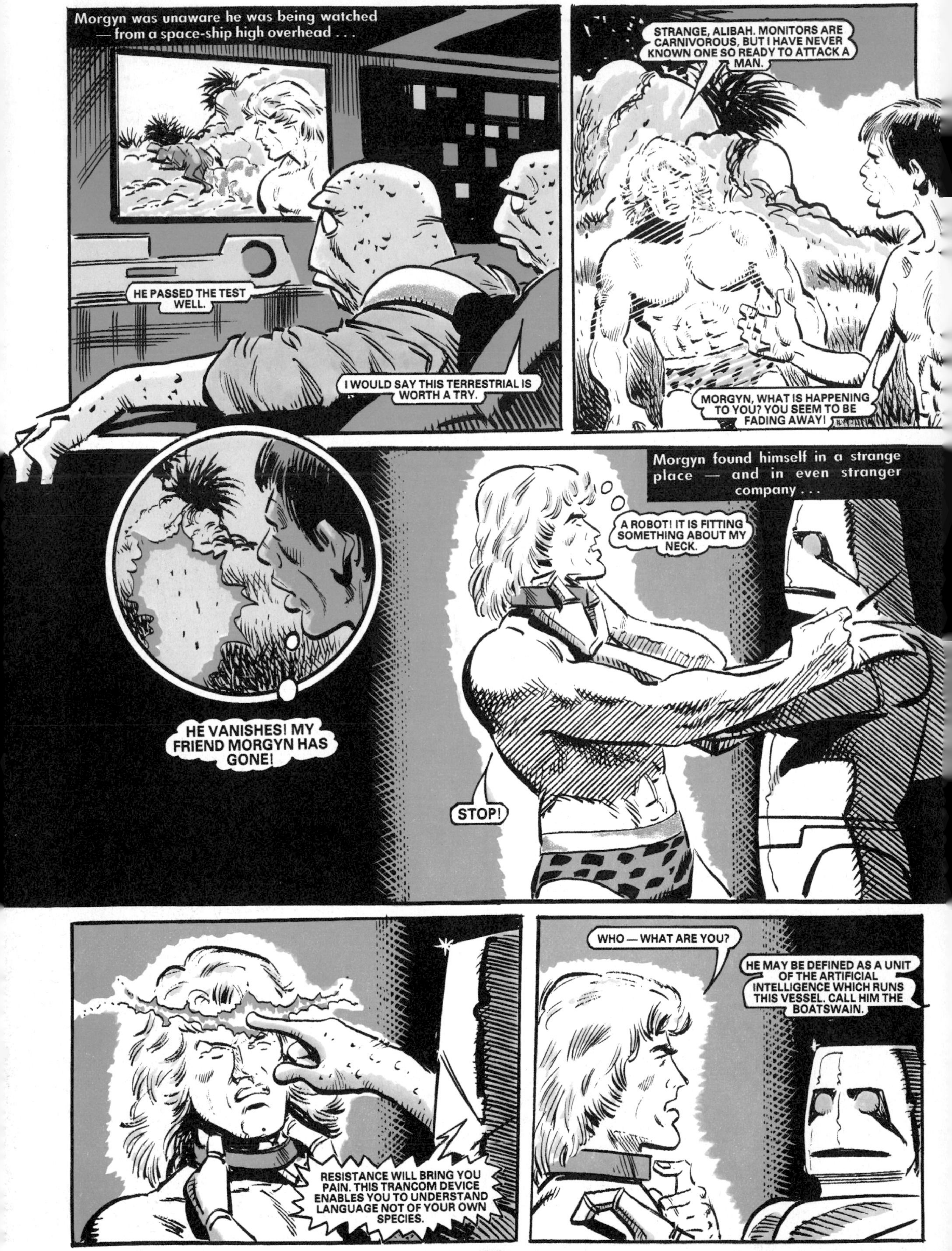

Morgyn was unaware he was being watched — from a space-ship high overhead . . .

HE PASSED THE TEST WELL.

I WOULD SAY THIS TERRESTRIAL IS WORTH A TRY.

STRANGE, ALIBAH. MONITORS ARE CARNIVOROUS, BUT I HAVE NEVER KNOWN ONE SO READY TO ATTACK A MAN.

MORGYN, WHAT IS HAPPENING TO YOU? YOU SEEM TO BE FADING AWAY!

HE VANISHES! MY FRIEND MORGYN HAS GONE!

Morgyn found himself in a strange place — and in even stranger company . . .

A ROBOT! IT IS FITTING SOMETHING ABOUT MY NECK.

STOP!

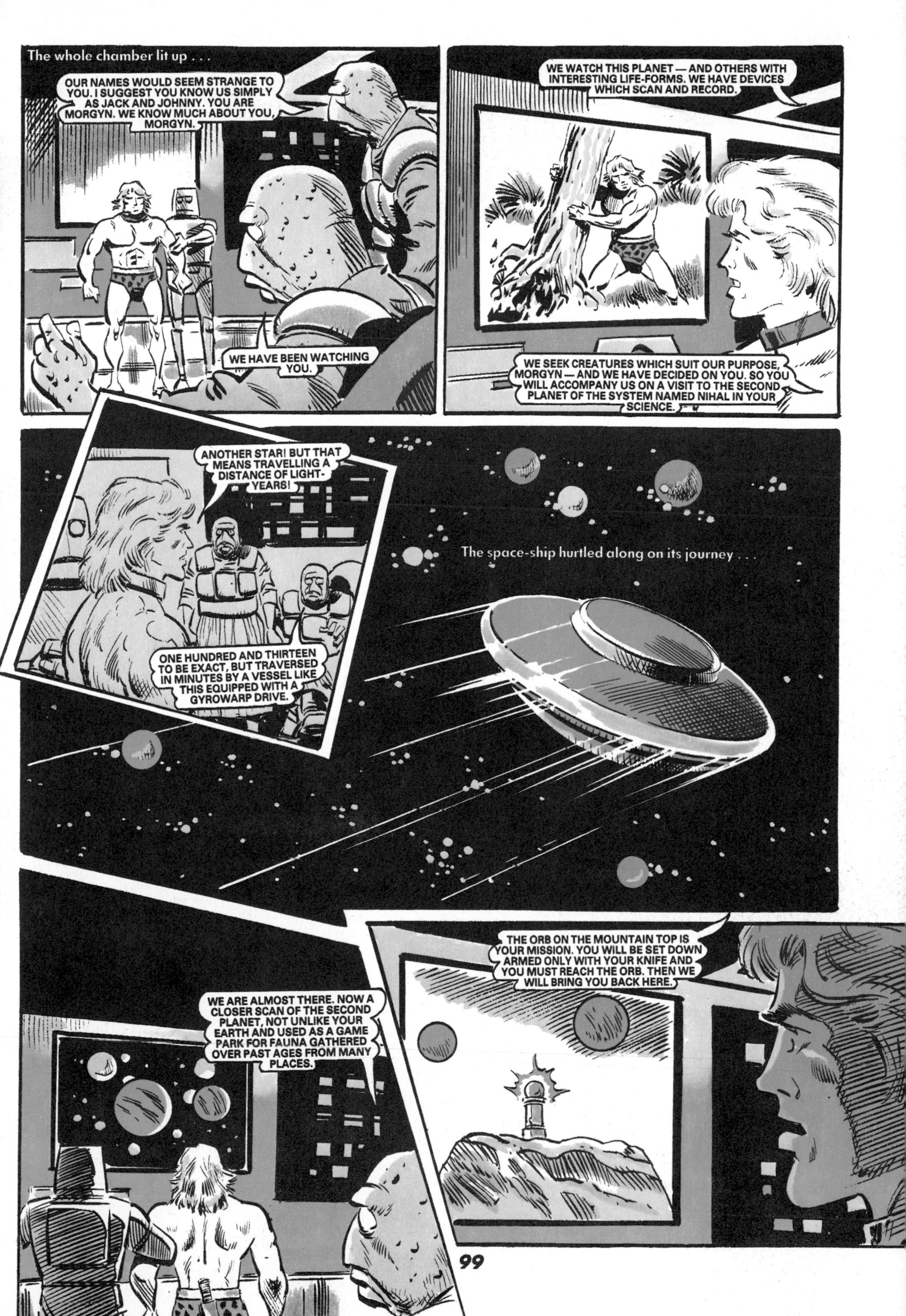
The whole chamber lit up . . .
OUR NAMES WOULD SEEM STRANGE TO YOU. I SUGGEST YOU KNOW US SIMPLY AS JACK AND JOHNNY. YOU ARE MORGYN. WE KNOW MUCH ABOUT YOU, MORGYN.
WE HAVE BEEN WATCHING YOU.
WE WATCH THIS PLANET — AND OTHERS WITH INTERESTING LIFE-FORMS. WE HAVE DEVICES WHICH SCAN AND RECORD.
WE SEEK CREATURES WHICH SUIT OUR PURPOSE, MORGYN — AND WE HAVE DECIDED ON YOU. SO YOU WILL ACCOMPANY US ON A VISIT TO THE SECOND PLANET OF THE SYSTEM NAMED NIHAL IN YOUR SCIENCE.
ANOTHER STAR! BUT THAT MEANS TRAVELLING A DISTANCE OF LIGHT-YEARS!
ONE HUNDRED AND THIRTEEN TO BE EXACT, BUT TRAVERSED IN MINUTES BY A VESSEL LIKE THIS EQUIPPED WITH A GYROWARP DRIVE.
The space-ship hurtled along on its journey . . .
WE ARE ALMOST THERE. NOW A CLOSER SCAN OF THE SECOND PLANET, NOT UNLIKE YOUR EARTH AND USED AS A GAME PARK FOR FAUNA GATHERED OVER PAST AGES FROM MANY PLACES.
THE ORB ON THE MOUNTAIN TOP IS YOUR MISSION. YOU WILL BE SET DOWN ARMED ONLY WITH YOUR KNIFE AND YOU MUST REACH THE ORB. THEN WE WILL BRING YOU BACK HERE.

SUPPOSE I REFUSE?
THEN NIHAL-TWO WILL BECOME YOUR HOME — FOR THE SHORT-TIME YOU WILL BE ABLE TO LIVE.
The robot released Morgyn . . .
. . . and he found himself beamed down on to the strange planet!
IT SEEMS I HAVE BECOME A PAWN IN A GAME BEING PLAYED BY A PAIR OF ALIEN GAMESTERS. I FANCY I'M GOING TO NEED MY KNIFE.
THE ORB! I HAVE TO REACH IT IF I AM TO HAVE ANY CHANCE OF GETTING OFF THIS PLANET.
HE IS ON HIS WAY. IS HE YET IN HAZARD?
IMMEDIATE HAZARD. WATCH.
WHAT THE —?
Cable-like tendrils suddenly snaked about Morgyn!

SOME VARIETY OF FLESH-EATING PLANT — AND THIS SAPLING ISN'T GOING TO HOLD ME FOR LONG!
THE SAPLING IS BREAKING FREE!
AT LEAST I'VE GOT A GOOD KNIFE. I'LL SHARPEN THE END OF THE TREE!
I'LL WEDGE THE MOUTH OPEN. THAT'LL GIVE ME TIME!
HE'S CUT HIMSELF FREE. VERY GOOD. I HAVE GREAT HOPES OF MORGYN.
HE STILL HAS SOME WAY TO GO.

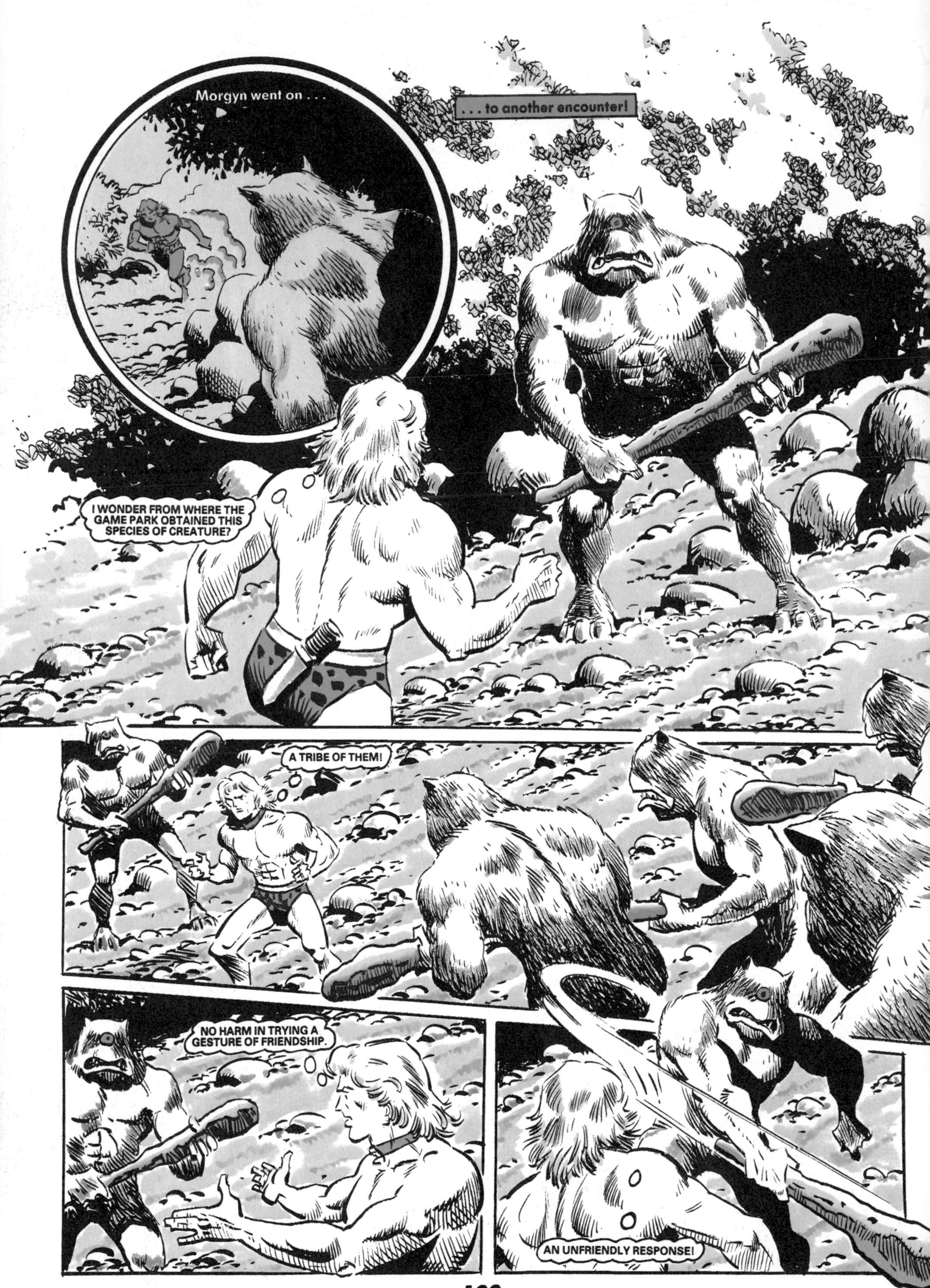
Morgyn went on . . .
. . . to another encounter!
I WONDER FROM WHERE THE GAME PARK OBTAINED THIS SPECIES OF CREATURE?
A TRIBE OF THEM!
NO HARM IN TRYING A GESTURE OF FRIENDSHIP.
AN UNFRIENDLY RESPONSE!

SORRY, BOYS — I'VE GOT TO GO!

A CHASE! I LIKE IT!

A GORGE — DEEP AND TOO WIDE TO JUMP.

Morgyn applied his strength to the problem . . .
A BRIDGE SEEMS CALLED FOR.

THEY'RE STILL COMING!

CONTINUED ON PAGE 106

DAYS OF THE GIANTS

Millions of years ago giants stalked the Earth. They were the dinosaurs, creatures far bigger and more ferocious than any living today.

The Brachiosaurus was the biggest dinosaur of all, weighing about fifty tons. From head to tail it was eighty feet long and stood over twice as high as a double-decker bus!

The Pteranodon was the size of a small aeroplane, with a wingspan of twenty-seven feet. This toothless, long-beaked reptile was the largest creature ever to fly.

The Tyrannosaurus Rex was the biggest, fiercest meat-eating animal ever to exist. Fifty feet long and standing twenty feet high, its dagger-like teeth were six inches long. The thirty-foot Triceratops was also a fearsome fighter, with a massive, curved shield of bone as protection and three stout horns for attack.

CONTINUED FROM PAGE 103

MISSED ME! AND I'VE REACHED THE ORB!
IT'S HEAVY! COULD BE PURE GOLD — AND HERE COMES THAT CREATURE AGAIN!
TAKE THAT!
I HAVE THE ORB. DO YOU HEAR ME?
Morgyn was beamed back aboard the space-ship . . .
HERE IS THE ORB. NOW RETURN ME TO MY OWN WORLD.
OH NO, MORGYN, YOU ARE MUCH TOO USEFUL TO US. WE ARE WHAT MIGHT BE TERMED SPORTING GENTLEMEN AND YOU ARE OUR CHAMPION,TO BE MATCHED AGAINST THE CHAMPIONS OF OTHERS OF OUR KIND WHO PLAY THIS LITTLE GAME OF HAZARD.
WHAT ABOUT THIS ORB?
OH THAT IS NOT IMPORTANT — MERELY A SYMBOL, A GOAL TO GIVE PURPOSE TO A CONTEST. YOU MAY PASS IT TO THE BOATSWAIN.

CERTAINLY — CATCH!
GENTLEMEN, I CAN KILL BOTH OF YOU BEFORE THE BOATSWAIN GETS TO US — AND I SHALL UNLESS YOU ORDER HIM TO TAKE ME HOME!
THIS IS IRREGULAR, MOST INCONVENIENT! BOATSWAIN, SET COURSE AT FULL GYROWARP FOR EARTH.
ARRIVAL SHOULD BE IN A MATTER OF TEN MINUTES. MORGYN — ER, DO PLEASE BE CAREFUL WITH THAT SHARP KNIFE.
YOUR HOME PLANET, MORGYN. YOU WILL BE BEAMED DOWN AND WE SHALL BE ON OUR WAY.
I WOULD FEEL MORE SECURE IF YOU GENTLEMEN CAME DOWN WITH ME. BOATSWAIN, YOU ARE TO LAND ALL THREE OF US AT THE LOCATION I INDICATE — AND YOU WILL THEN RUN THIS VESSEL INTO THE SUN.
BOATSWAIN, DISREGARD THAT ORDER!
DESTROY OUR SPACE-SHIP! MAROON US! OH NO, OUT OF THE QUESTION!

SO YOU WOULD PREFER TO DIE HERE AND NOW.
OH NO — NO!
CONFIRMATION OF ORDERS. TRANSPORT YOU DOWN. SET VESSEL ON DESTRUCTION COURSE WITH SUN.
YES — CURSE YOU, MORGYN — CONFIRMED!
Morgyn came back to Earth . . .
AT LEAST WE ARE IN AN INHABITED AREA.
A CONCRETE JUNGLE, GENTLEMEN, THE MOST DANGEROUS PLACE IN THE WORLD — NEW YORK CITY!
MORGYN, WE WOULD BE GRATEFUL FOR YOUR TRANCOM TO ENABLE US TO REACH UNDERSTANDING WITH THE NATIVES.
CAN'T UNDERSTAND WHAT YOU ARE SAYING NOW I HAVE TAKEN OFF THIS TRANCOM.
Morgyn was suddenly gone — but others came . . .
GUYS, LOOK AT 'EM. AIN'T THEY CUTE?
WHAT A PITY I CANNOT PROVIDE THEM WITH A GOLDEN ORB TO ADD INTEREST TO THIS LITTLE GAME!
The End

PUSS an BOOTS
in
A RIGHT OLD PANTOMIME!

SO HE'S AT IT AGAIN, IS HE? HIS GREAT UGLY MUG PLASTERED ALL OVER TOWN! DEAR-OH-DEAR, I'VE SEEN BETTER-LOOKING COMPOST HEAPS!
ALI BABA AND THE FORTY THIEVES WITH BOOTS
(STAR OF STAGE, SCREEN, RADIO AND SID'S PETROL PUMP)

GREETINGS THEATRE LOVERS! I AM ALI BABA AND I KNOW THE MAGIC WORDS WHICH WILL OPEN THE CAVE WHERE THE WICKED CROOKS HAVE HIDDEN THEIR LOOT! I THANK YOU!
HE'S GOT A LOVELY VOICE! YOU CAN MAKE OUT NEARLY EVERY WORD HE SAYS!

OPEN, SEZ ME!

TA-RUMPH!!!
THUNDER!
AAARGH! ELEPHANTS? THERE WEREN'T ANY ELEPHANTS AT REHEARSALS? BUT I SHALL CARRY ON AS IF NOTHING HAS HAPPENED, LIKE A TRUE PROFESSIONAL!

THIS WAY, JUMBOS! THAT STAGE-HAND MUST'VE GIVEN US THE WRONG DIRECTIONS!
STAGE-HAND? DIRECTIONS? ANYWAY, AS I WAS SAYIN', OPEN, SEZ ME!

IT WAS NICE OF THAT STAGE-HAND TO SHOW US BACKSTAGE!
LET'S GET BACK TO OUR SEATS NOW!
AYE, THE SHOW'LL BE STARTING SOON!
SHRIEK!
TRAMPLE!
TRAMPLE!

I BET SIR LAURENCE OLIVE OIL NEVER HAS THIS TROUBLE WHEN HE DOES PANTO!
AI-HEM! OPEN, SEZ ME!

AAARGH! NORRAGAIN!
EEE, THERE'S A LOT OF CLEANING UP TO DO! THE SHOW MUST'VE FINISHED EARLY!

HEY, WHAT'S GOIN'ON? THAT STAGE-HAND SAID IT WAS OKAY TO COME ON MIND YOU I DON'T THINK HE KNOWS WHAT HE'S DOIN'– PUTTIN' GUNPOWDER IN THE MAGIC LAMP LIKE THAT!
YOU CAN TAKE YOUR SOAPY WATER, MADAM, AND GO!... WAIT A MINUTE... WHAT WAS THAT ABOUT A STAGE-HAND?
PROD!

HEH-HEH! THEY'LL BOOT THAT MUTT RIGHT OUT OF THE THEATRE – IF HE'S STILL AROUND AFTER HE LIGHTS THIS MAGIC LAMP FULL OF NASTY BANG-BANG!
GRRR! AS I THOUGHT!

OOYA! HEY, MY TOOTH! THAT'S THE ONE I USE FOR CRACKIN' WALNUTS! OOH, YOU'VE REALLY DONE IT NOW! YOU REALLY HAVE!
YEAH! AN' I'M GONNA DO IT AGAIN! AN' AGAIN AN' AGAIN...
BLAP!

...AN' AGAIN AN' AGAIN AN' AGAIN...
ALL RIGHT- JUST ONCE MORE–THEN I'M GONNA GET REALLY ANGRY!
BOP!
SPLAT!
BLAT!
CRUMP!
HEY, IT'S THEM!
THIS IS BETTER THAN ANY PANTO!

AND SO-
PUSS an' BOOTS in
ALI BABA AND THE FORTY THIEVES
PUNCH UPS!
AN' ANOTHER THING! TAKE THAT!
OUCH! YOU'RE REPEATING YOURSELF! YOU GAVE ME ONE OF THESE A WEEK PAST FRIDAY! OOHYA!
I DON'T KNOW HOW THEY DO IT! THEY HAVEN'T EVEN STOPPED FOR A CUPPA TEA!
6TH TREMENDOUS WEEK
HOUSE FULL

Photo Fun

Have a laugh at these funny sports photographs and the daft balloons that go with them!

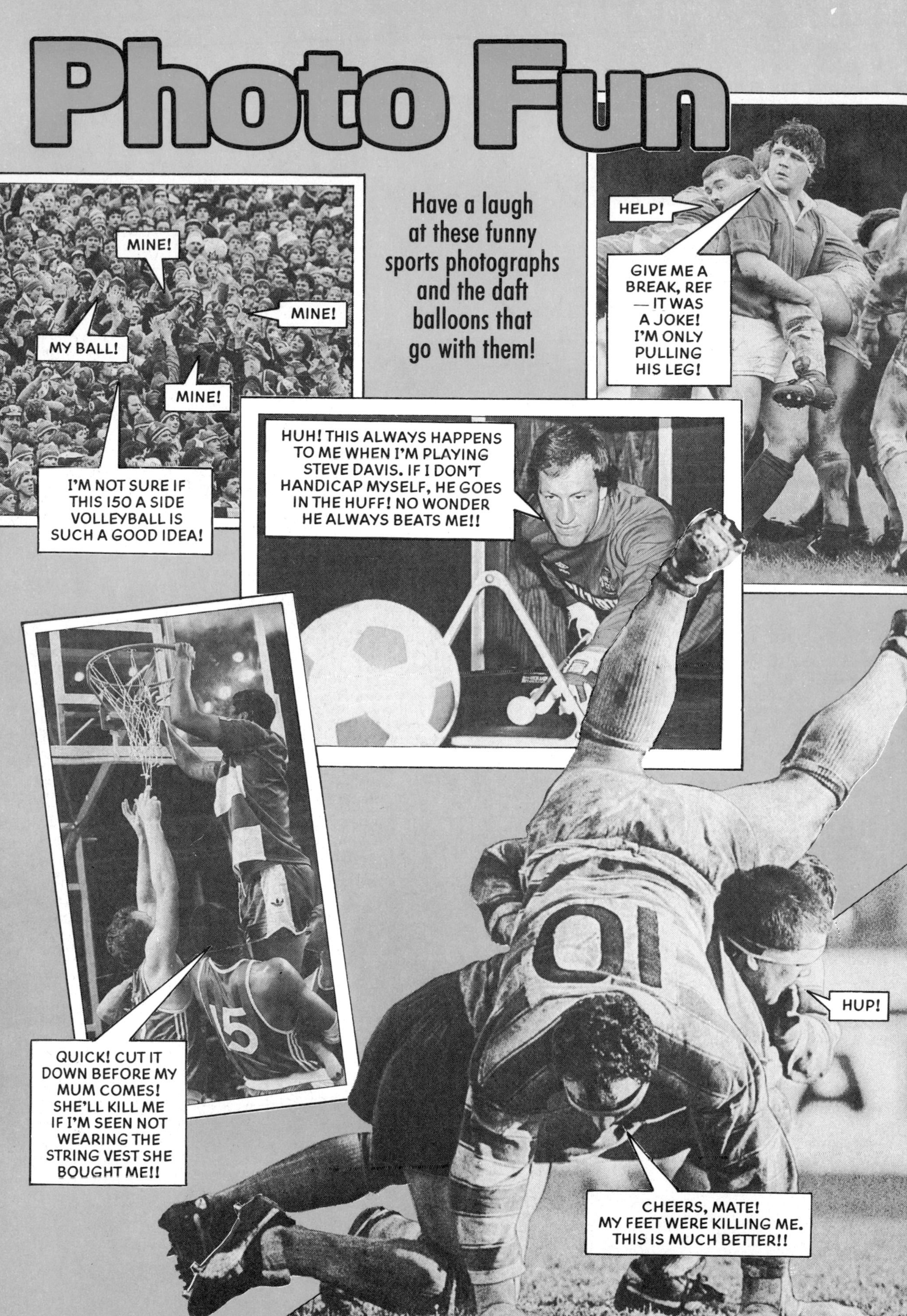

STARK
MATCHWINNER FOR HIRE
JON STARK
£3000 PER MATCH
PLUS £250 PER GOAL
NO PAYMENT FOR LOST GAME
Jon Stark, soccer mercenary, signed one-match contracts and played all over the world. Now he was playing for San Jose Eagles in Mexico. With one minute to go, there was no score. Then Stark pounced . . .
EAGLES WIN!
GOALLLLLLLLL! JON STARK!
EL NINO
GRANDE
GARUA

WE SEE YOU SOON, SENOR STARK? EAGLES WILL BUY YOUR SERVICES AGAIN, YES?
HOTEL
GRANDE
I HOPE SO, LUIS! BUT RIGHT NOW I'M HEADING BACK TO EUROPE! I'VE A FEW GAMES LINED UP OVER THERE!
Three days later . . .
BLACKTON! MY HOME TOWN! THE OLD PLACE NEVER CHANGES!
Blackton Rovers' ground . . .
JON STARK! GOOD TO SEE YOU, MAN! WHAT ARE YOU DOING HERE? ROVERS CAN'T AFFORD TO SIGN YOU!
JUST LOOKED IN, JIM! HEARD YOU WERE IN TROUBLE! IN THE RELEGATION ZONE . . .
IT'S BEEN A BAD YEAR, JON. LOTS OF INJURIES. GOT A LOT OF GOOD YOUNGSTERS, BUT THEY NEED ANOTHER SEASON BEFORE THEY BLOSSOM!
BE A SHAME IF ROVERS GO DOWN! NOT ONLY BAD FOR THE CLUB BUT BAD FOR THE TOWN.
EXIT
IF YOU WANT ME, JIM, I'LL PLAY FOR BLACKTON — NO CHARGE! I RECKON I OWE THIS CLUB. I LEARNED MY FOOTBALL HERE.
YOU'RE ON, JON. TURN OUT ON SATURDAY AND WHEN THE WORD GETS ROUND, WE'LL HAVE THE BIGGEST GATE OF THE SEASON!
Saturday. Blackton Rovers versus Liverford.
JON STARK! JON STARK!
BALDIE JAMES! SAME AS EVER! A NUDGE IN THE BACK TO KEEP YOU OFF BALANCE! ON THE BLIND SIDE!

And . . .
UNNGH!
FULL OF FIRE FOR THE FIRST FIFTEEN MINUTES! THEN HE GOES OFF THE BOIL!
WHAT THE . . . ?
GOALIE'S WELL OFF HIS LINE . . .
IT'S THERE! WHAT A LOB FROM STARK!
LEAVE IT OUT, JON! THEY'LL GIVE ME A HARD TIME FOR THAT NOW!
Late in the second half . . .
KEEP GOING, BRIAN! YOU'RE AWAY!
I KNOW BRIAN JOHNSON'S GAME! WHEN HE CROSSES 'EM, THEY'RE HARD AND LOW!
MAGIC! THAT'S JON STARK FOR YOU! MAKES 'EM OUT OF NOTHING!

YESSSSSSS!
JON STARK AGAIN! TWO-NIL!
YOU GOT US THREE POINTS TODAY, JON! HOW ABOUT NEXT SATURDAY . . . AWAY TO TOTTENFORD?
SURE! I'M IN FRANCE TOMORROW, BUT I'LL GET BACK!
Next day at St Valery F.C.
YOU PLAYED YESTERDAY IN ENGLAND! YOU CAN'T PLAY TWO GAMES IN TWO DAYS!
WHO SAYS I CAN'T? NOTHING TO IT, MISTER!
I SAY YOU CAN'T! IT IS TOO MUCH!
DRESSING ROOMS
I'LL SEE ST VALERY WIN, CHUM! IF THEY LOSE, I DON'T GET PAID, AND I'VE GOT MY PLANE FARE TO PAY!
St Valery versus Bordaigne F.C.
YEAHHHH! GOOD BALL, PIERRE!
TYPICAL CONTINENTAL FOOTBALL! SLOW BUILD-UP . . . KEEP POSSESSION! BUT, YOU JUST HAVE TO WAIT . . .
. . . UNTIL THE CHANCE COMES TO POUNCE!
OHHHH! THE ENGLISHMAN'S INTERCEPTED!

Jon suddenly accelerated!
JEAN-CLAUDE CAN'T CATCH HIM.
GOT 'EM WORRIED . . .
IT'S THERE! WHAT A SHOT! JON STARK!
THAT SHOOK 'EM! ALL LOOKING FOR ME TO PASS!
Second half . . .
CORNER!
BORDAIGNE! BORDAIGNE!
ANOTHER CORNER!
OUR GOALIE'S PLAYING A BLINDER! BUT HE CAN'T KEEP DOING IT! WE NEED ANOTHER ONE TO MAKE IT SAFE!
St Valery moved forward . . .
TACKLE HIM! DON'T LET HIM SHOOT!
I HAVEN'T DRAWN THESE TWO BLOKES OUT HERE TO HIT ONE FROM AN IMPOSSIBLE ANGLE, MATE!
ROGER LETREVE LIKES 'EM OVER THERE! WHERE IS HE?

CONTINUED ON PAGE 120

MARK HUGHES

(1) Mark Hughes is English, Welsh or Lithuanian?
(2) Does Mark normally play in defence, midfield or attack?
(3) Name the Spanish club for which he played.
(4) His nickname is Boots, Poacher or Sparky?
(5) He won the P.F.A. Young Player of the Year award in 1984, 1985 or 1989?

ANSWERS ON PAGE 63

CONTINUED FROM PAGE 118

YES, JON, MY DIRECTORS HAVE HEARD OF YOU! BUT THEY INSIST UPON MEETING YOU BEFORE THEY CONTRACT YOU TO PLAY FOR BASTERRA!
OKAY, PEDRO! I'LL BE DOWN THERE TOMORROW AFTERNOON . . .
THIS IS GONNA MAKE IT TOUGH GETTING BACK TO BLACKTON FOR SATURDAY'S MATCH!
Saturday morning in Blackton . . .
I HOPE JON STARK GETS HERE, MR HASTINGS! THIS FOG COULD HOLD HIM UP. I EXPECT HE'S FLYING IN FROM SOMEWHERE, ISN'T HE?
FROM SPAIN! IF HE'S NOT HERE BY KICK-OFF TIME, I'LL PUT HIM DOWN AS SUB AND HOPE FOR THE BEST!
Stark had reached France . . .
DO ME A FAVOUR, BENNY! FLY ME TO ENGLAND! THE COMMERCIAL AIRCRAFT ARE RUNNING DELAYS AS LONG AS MY ARM! IT'S URGENT!
FOR YOU, STARKY . . . I WILL! ALL I WANT IS HALF A DOZEN TICKETS FOR THE CUP FINAL AT WEMBLEY THIS YEAR! DEAL?
I SUPPOSE YOU KNOW WHERE WE ARE, BENNY? I WANT BLACKTON! THEY KICKED OFF TEN MINUTES AGO!
TRUST ME!
Twenty minutes later . . .
I PUT YOU DOWN AS SUB, JON. GET THIS NUMBER TWELVE SHIRT ON. WE'RE ONE-NIL DOWN ALREADY!
OKAY! LET'S GO!
SUBSTITUTING FOR KEVIN PRICE . . . NUMBER TWELVE . . . JON STARK!
GOOD LUCK, JON!
ONE DOWN AND NEARLY THROUGH THE FIRST HALF! WE'RE GONNA NEED IT!
LARRY WALLIS! PLAYED AGAINST HIM BEFORE! SOLID DEFENDER . . . BUT NO LEFT FOOT!

YEAHHH! YOU'RE PAST HIM, JON!
DONE HIM!
IT'S THERE! MAGIC PASS FROM STARK!
Second half . . .
STARK! STARK! JON STARK!
CHOP HIM DOWN!
CAN'T BE MORE THAN A MINUTE TO GO! IT'S NOW OR NEVER!
IT'S THERE! HE'S DONE IT! WE'VE WON!

ALL WE NEED IS THREE POINTS FROM OUR LAST TWO GAMES! AND WE STAY UP!
LET'S GET THOSE THREE POINTS IN THE NEXT MATCH, JIM. DON'T WANT TO LEAVE IT TO THE LAST GAME!
Blackton's second last game was against high-flying Rexford United. At half-time it was 1-1, Jon Stark having scored for Blackton.
In the second half . . .
A GOOD TACKLE FROM YOUNG ANDY JONES.
AND A GREAT PASS DOWN THE WING.
NOW PASS IT HERE, NICK!
But Nick decided to shoot.
HE'S MISSED! HE'D NO CHANCE FROM THAT ANGLE! BUT A LITTLE MORE EXPERIENCE WILL SHOW HIM WHAT HE CAN AND CAN'T DO!

Then Rexford showed their class!
GOOD GOAL. AND WE'VE NOT GOT LONG TO SAVE THE GAME!
Not long enough!
WE'VE LOST! SO IT'S ALL ON THE LAST GAME!
The last game was at home against Canchester City.
ROVERS
STARK'S HERE. FLEW IN AFTER A MIDWEEK GAME FOR BASTERRA.
WE NEED HIM. IF WE DON'T BEAT CITY, IT'S BYE-BYE FIRST DIVISION FOOTBALL!
No favours from City!
BOOOOOO!
UURGH!
Free-kick . . . to the far post!
IT'S THERE! JON STARK'S HEADER!
Blackton on the rampage!
CHASE IT, NICK!

YEAHHHHHH! TWO-NIL!
NICK'S LEARNED FROM HIS MISTAKE IN THE LAST GAME!
Near the end . . .
LET'S SEE IF I CAN PUT THE ICING ON THE CAKE! GIVE 'EM SOMETHING TO CHEER ABOUT! THEY'VE HAD A TOUGH SEASON!
HE'S GONE ROUND THE GOALIE! GOT TO BE NUMBER THREE!
WALK ON . . . WALK ON . . . AND YOU'LL NEVER WALK ALONE . . .
Later . . .
YOUR YOUNGSTERS WILL COME GOOD NEXT SEASON. THEY'LL KEEP YOU IN THE FIRST DIVISION! LIKE I SAID, I OWE BLACKTON FOR GIVING ME MY START IN THE GAME YEARS AGO.
IT'S BLACKTON WHO OWE YOU!
'BYE! GOT TO GO . . . GOT A TIGHT SCHEDULE!
THE END

SPORT, WAR A